MISSION
IMPROBABLE

THE MEMOIRS
OF
PROF DAVID I HAMILTON FRCS

© Hamilton Press 2009

British Library Cataloguing in Publication Data.
A full CIP record for this book is available from the British Library
ISBN 978 0 956237 6 06

Printed by Bootle Print
England

CONTENTS

D I Hamilton, FRCS

A SURGEON'S WORK

Who would want the life of a surgeon?
I know a man who dedicated
his life to that work.
A life given for the life of others.
Men, women and children all
benefited from his deftness
and slight of hand.

The long late nights,
the standing and bending
his confidence and skill
all for the chance to live.
And most of them did.

His reputation went before him
and they travelled from all corners
seeking his expertise.
Better than "Ormond St." they said,
but his team never publicised the fact.

His eyes, sharp and bright,
put many of nature's defects right
and his knife was sharper than a sword
his wit was dryer than desert sand.
His stories were many.

I know a man who gave himself
to the life of a surgeon.
I know a man who gave his life
so that others might live.

I know another man like that,
Do You?

Al Hamilton   2008

John A.K. Hamilton,
G.M., DSc.(Edin.Hon.), F.H.-W.C., M.I.C.E., M.I.Mcc.E.

Helen Eliza Bruce Kirk

ACKNOWLEDGEMENTS

These memoirs have been compiled for our grandchildren, Jake, Morgan, Scott, Esme and Leonardo and for our own sons, Ian, James, Al and Ross. A number of doctors from overseas have suggested that I should tell my story.

I dedicate this book to Myra in gratitude for our life together and for making my mission possible. There may be some readers who are interested to hear of the way in which my boyhood ambitions were achieved. In the longer term, those studying medical training in the period in which I write may find some points of interest. Times have changed and training is very different in each generation. It has not been possible to include the names of all those who have accompanied me on my mission. I want them to know that each person's involvement in the team has been of critical importance to our patient's safe passage through surgery.

For the surgeon, teamwork starts at home. That is why one of my ambitions was to "marry the right girl." Myra has supported me over sixty years, often single-handed, when I was not available to carry out my share of household duties. She has shouldered the main burden of bringing up our family. I have, in fact, had two families, my own and my patients in hospital. I would not have been able to do my job to professional standard if I had not been properly looked after at home. I was fortunate in my choice of parents! They were exceptional people setting us a fine example in living and in their service to others. They were generous in their provision for us. Our spiritual and physical well-being were important to them. They encouraged us to develop our natural abilities, to be constructive rather than destructive, and to care for those less fortunate than ourselves. My grandmother was a skilful needlewoman and she had embroidered a sampler in different coloured silks. Below was the saying, "Not failure, but low aim is crime." On the other hand my mother warned against striving above one's natural ability. A chain is as strong as its weakest link. I estimate that a child who undergoes open heart surgery is supported by at least fifty experts in a wide spectrum of specialities on the day of their operation. These include, surgeons, cardiologists, anaesthetists, nursing staff in the theatre, intensive care ward staff, radiologists, radiographers, physiotherapists, ECG technicians and experts working in the blood transfusion service. The pathology department supply vital information from the analysis of blood samples taken from the patient before, during and after their operation.

Having a heart operation is no excuse for taking time off school! The more active units providing cardiac services should have "in house" educational facilities within the hospital or close by. It is important to remember those who keep the hospital running in good order. The list is never ending as we remember engineers, electricians, plumbers and telephonists who provide the twenty four hour service. If I have failed to mention other particular contributions, this is due to a failing memory and is not intentional. Efficient secretarial and data processing services are necessary for the smooth running of a modern cardiac unit. Keeping pace with other centres throughout the world entails presenting summaries of the team's results in printed articles and as papers given verbatim at Symposia and International meetings.

What we achieved was important to those who benefited from our skills and experiences, the difference between life and death in fact. I have included the poem, "The Dead Child" by George Barlow, because it reminds us of the importance of working to the highest standards day by day.

Human error can never be eliminated entirely but it can be minimised by concentration and vigilance. Two quotations are appropriate in this context.

Psalm 127: "Except the Lord build the house, they labour in vain, that build it."

The Prayer of St. Teresa should put our work in correct context: "Christ has no body on earth but yours, no hands but yours, no feet but yours. Yours are the eyes through which is to look out God's compassion to the world. Yours are the feet with which He is to go about doing good and yours are the hands with which He is to bless us now."

May God go with you day by day.

Our sincere thanks to Sarah White for reading the text and for her helpful suggestions before going to press. Tom Wayles played a major role in the design of the outer cover of these Memoirs. For this, 'many thanks.'

EARLY RECOLLECTIONS

The story I have to tell is a true account of my life work as a cardiac surgeon and of the chain of events that enabled me to realise three boyhood ambitions; to become a member of The Royal College of Surgeons, to play international rugby football and to make sure that I married the "right girl!" This was a triumvirate of aspirations that might well have proved too much for a young boy. I struggled at school with some subjects and achieved more on the playing field than in the classroom. These ambitions were not the romantic dreams of an imaginative youthful spirit as each was built on sound foundations. Neither are they presented here in order of importance. However, the first always took precedence over the second and the adage "knife before wife" had not alerted us to a problem that has destroyed many promising careers in surgery.

These memoirs record how my objectives were achieved: how help was at hand when needed, how "things" happened at the right time and how a thread of purpose went ahead of me, encouraging me to keep pressing on towards my mission.

I was born on the 22nd June 1931 at 6pm in a nursing home in Stockton-on-Tees, a son for Jack and Helen Hamilton, of The Grove, Marton, near Middlesborough and a younger brother for Katherine Anne. My parents, John Alexander King Hamilton and Helen Hamilton (nee Helen Eliza Bruce Kirk) married in 1927 when mother was thirty five and father twenty seven. My father had been brought up in the Quaker tradition of worship. He was a pupil at Bootham School in York the largest school for boys in the country run by the Society of Friends. His time there coincided with the Great War and at the age of seventeen he decided that it was time for him to make a personal contribution to the war in Europe. To make himself acceptable for recruitment into the British services he falsified his age by one year and applied to the Friends Ambulance Unit (FAU) that was active in France. Nevertheless he was refused due to his age. These men and women supported British and Overseas troops in the heat of battle risking their own lives to bring the dead, dying and wounded back to base hospitals and casualty clearing centres. So many young men were eager to get to France at this time. Little did they know what mayhem they were to experience. My Father was accepted into the category of "non-combatant" as an ambulance driver by the French Red Cross. This enabled him to learn

French that he enjoyed speaking in later life on subsequent visits to France. Once he passed his eighteenth birthday he was transferred to the FAU.

It came to light later that he would have been mentioned in dispatches and possibly decorated for a specific act of bravery but we learned years later that this was withheld as he was classified as "non-combatant." His life was spared when he returned to his billet one evening when it was dark. His camp bed was above a stable and was reached by a flight of wooden stairs that he had started to climb. A voice called out,

"Who goes there?"

"Jack Hamilton" was his reply.

"Thank God for that, we have been looking for you since the billet was shelled less than an hour ago!"

My father was a civil engineer who specialised in bridge building. He had joined the Scottish firm of consulting engineers, Mott, Hay and Anderson after the First World War. Years later he became a senior partner in the firm. He worked on the arch bridge at Newcastle-upon-Tyne which was opened in 1930 and was the forerunner to the Sydney Harbour Bridge. He then moved to Middlesborough and was again resident engineer throughout the construction of this remarkable feat of engineering. The centre span carrying the roadway could be raised and lowered at the press of a button allowing ships to pass. Pulley wheels were mounted near the top of each tower around which steel ropes passed. When a button was pressed in the control tower the pulley wheels wound up the steel hawsers and the roadway on the centre span was raised. Shipping could then pass.

This bridge was a truly remarkable triumph of British bridge building. The bridge was to form a link between Middlesborough and the county of Durham. It was the largest of its type in the world and unique in this country. The bridge cost £512,000. The main span which rises to a height of 120 feet above high water weighs 2,700 tons. The moving weight when being lifted is 5,400 tons. The bridge was opened by The Duke and Duchess of York in February 1934. My father was one of the people to describe the working of the bridge to the Duchess. "Have we really started?" she questioned. The bridge moved so smoothly without any extraneous noise that the Duchess asked, "Are we actually moving?" The first vessel to pass under the bridge was the Aclan Cross, the only electric tug on the Tees. The lowest tender that was accepted in December 1930 was submitted by Messrs Dorman, Long and Co. The contract was signed in June 1931 and specified the completion of the bridge within thirty-three months and this was accomplished. The lifting machinery was supplied by Messrs Broadbents of Huddersfield. The Igranic Electric Co. Ltd of Bedford supplied the electric equipment.

During the construction of this bridge my father would take me on a conducted tour, usually at the weekend. He tucked me under his arm and carried me over planks and unfinished steel structure to reach the safe haven of the control cabin. I was then allowed to assume the role of "duty engineer" who was responsible for the safe passage of ships on the river. Taking on this role was scarcely adequate compensation for the trauma of being carried high above the river in the fashion of Charles Blondin, the famous rope-walker. I think my father would have been severely reprimanded by my mother had she known of these undeniably risky exploits. However, I found my father's fearlessness allied with his gymnastic agility an inspiration. His reputation for achievement as a professional bridge engineer was widely recognized.

My father could be tough and was a difficult adversary when roused! His courage was honoured during the Second World War when he was seconded to London County Council by his firm of consulting Engineers. He found himself one day leading a team of bomb disposal experts who had been delegated the task of removing a 1,000kg unexploded German bomb from nearby sewage and gas instillations in West London. Being the younger of his two children, I was not able to accompany him to Buckingham Palace for the investiture by King George VI when he received the George medal. I was immensely proud of my father and would love to have been by his side on that occasion.

My mother was the youngest of six children born to The Reverend John Kirk and his wife Eliza. They lived in Hopefield, Greenhill Gardens, Bruntsfield, Edinburgh. The house was built by my great-grandfather, The Reverend Professor John Kirk. He exercised the gift of healing and his writings bear witness to his amazing success in this field using simple, common sense treatments. Three of my mother's four brothers became doctors. Two served as missionary surgeons in China. Uncle John Kirk subsequently held the chair of Anatomy at the Middlesex Hospital Medical

Newport Bridge, River Tees 1934

School in London. After returning from the mission field he ran courses with Professor Samson Wright in Anatomy and Physiology. These courses were immensely popular with young doctors who were studying for the examination in the Primary Surgical Fellowship. Uncle Edward, Doctor E W Kirk, was imprisoned in Stanley camp when the Japanese invaded Hong Kong. His family escaped by catching the last boat to sail from the island. He elected to stay and performed the surgical operations that were necessary during the years of the occupation.

Mother trained in nursing and midwifery at Edinburgh Royal Infirmary. She worked in Damascus and became a sister tutor in Leeds. She was an accomplished violinist and pianist. Her faith and sense of humour sustained her throughout her life. She took her responsibilities as a parent seriously, committing herself unsparingly to the demands of family life. She was interested in our education, in poetry, music and literature. She was faithful in passing on to her children her beliefs and interpretation of the Gospel which sustained her throughout her life.

My mother's holiday home when she was a girl was Ardniel House, now "Kirkfields" which is situated on the Ayreshire coast at West Kilbride. The house overlooks the golf course and, in the distance, is the Isle of Arran. The children all grew up to play golf. Uncle John became a scratch player and represented Edinburgh University as a student. Mother bought me a half set of hickory-shafted clubs for my sixth birthday and I became a keen player. Whilst I doubt if mother ever held a club handicap, she had a fine rhythmical swing learnt from her brothers as she "stotted" her ball along behind them. She was adept at finding balls in the rough. I returned home one evening on my bicycle, and told her that I had lost two balls at the same hole. She immediately left her work in the kitchen and applied herself to searching for the lost items. Within about fifteen minutes she had found thirteen golf balls and my disappointment had turned to joy. This was typical of the support she gave us as we grew up.

On a more serious note I owe my life to my mother in more ways than one. Due to her cool head and prompt action she saved me from a potentially lethal situation before I could walk. I had developed a method of progression that involved shuffling around the floor on my behind with one leg tucked under my seat and the other in front of me. Mother had prepared a trolley for afternoon tea for a number of guests. She pushed the trolley into the lounge where I was sitting on the floor, keeping Bruno, our

Labrador, company. When she returned to the kitchen, I seized my moment of opportunity, and shuffled across the floor on my behind as fast as I could go until I reached my goal. On the lower shelf of the trolley was a basin of white sugar lumps. In a few moments I pushed about eight lumps into my mouth with such force that some became impacted in my larynx. When mother returned from the kitchen she found me partially asphyxiated, clearly in severe danger of complete obstruction of the airway. Realising this, she took immediate action, as time was of the essence. Tipping me upside down by the feet she clapped me on my back firmly and hooked the heavily blood stained cubes out of my mouth and pharynx with her long fingers. Air was now able to enter my lungs and my colour reverted to a normal pink complexion and the wheezing ceased. "What a ghastly moment that was!"

My mother was a "daughter of the manse" and attended her father's church. However for the first twenty years of her marriage she supported her husband in accompanying him to Quaker meetings on Sunday mornings. Consequently, my sister Anne and I were brought up in the Quaker tradition. We worshipped in the Meeting House at Great Ayton School in Yorkshire, at Wandsworth in South London and in a private house in Wimbledon during the Blitz. I then came under the Quaker influence at Leighton Park School in Reading. This is a difficult way to worship for young people. Before their teens, they attend meeting for ten to fifteen minutes before they are "released" to Sunday school. Here they are taught from the bible and usually activities follow. Quaker worship is based on silence. Members of meeting listen to the voice of God who guides, inspires and refreshes our spirit. The "inner light" dwells within us and the Comforter is available to us at all times. Anyone attending meeting on Sunday is entitled to address those present, giving the message that is in their minds at that particular time.

I spent the first five and a half years of my life with the family living in The Grove, Marton, south of Middlesborough. One of my vivid recollections of that time is of walks in Stewarts Park to see the ducks. If we had behaved well we were allowed to climb up to the large house on the hill to purchase the most delicious ice-cream cornets. Ice cream has never tasted better and remains a favourite of mine to this day. We used to walk across the fields to wave to the express trains as they thundered past at great speed on their journey South to London. One day, we were cornered beside the gate into a field by a herd of cows that jostled us and threatened to knock us over.

On another occasion a number of young bullocks got into our front garden and rapidly destroyed the daffodils and turned the front lawn into a quagmire.

My main mode of transport at this time was a pedal car that I used to fill up with petrol at an imaginary pump at the side of the garage. Bruno would lie in the middle of the road waiting for my father to return home from work in his motor car. Suddenly his tail would begin to thump against the tarmac and I wondered what had got into him. Some few hundred yards up the road there was a right-angled bend. Cars then disappeared out of sight and earshot. When my father was returning home his car would sweep round this corner. Bruno's hearing was more acute than mine enabling him to recognize the characteristic sound of my father's car engine before I could see or hear the vehicle. Bruno was a splendid companion and excelled as a gun dog on Saturdays when my father went rough shooting over a farm at Bedale.

My sister Anne and I were pupils at primary school in the village of Nunthorpe. The Headmistress was Mrs Mallion. Mother took us in her Morris Cowley when the weather was fine, otherwise we would travel the short distance by train. We usually travelled with other pupils and we had a great game making "tents" out of the seats. The backs of these seats could be moved forwards or backwards to make hideouts.

I have two memories in particular of this time. The first was of sitting on a wooden seat learning the alphabet and "numbers" using beads and letters that were mounted on a frame. The second is of following an outside trail that had been laid by the older pupils for their younger brothers and sisters. These treasure hunts pursued their course through woods and fields around the school.

Three of my grandparents were of Scottish descent. My paternal grandmother, Ethel Tisdall, being the exception, was English born and bred. Her husband, Dr John Hamilton, was a Scot, a Quaker, as was my father, and a general practitioner. He was interested in homoeopathic medicine and was apparently an excellent diagnostician. He built up several practices successfully, including one in Newcastle and another in Chester Square, London. He was a founder member of the Temperance Movement, enjoyed travel and sold his practice on more than one occasion to take up appointments as ships surgeon. He sailed to various corners of the globe, including USA and Canada. Ethel Tisdall was the only grandparent I knew. She died when I was thirteen and in my early days as a border at Leighton Park School, Reading, Berkshire. I got into trouble with my father for delaying my reply to his letter that brought me the sad news. I knew he was very upset but I could not find the words to console him in his grief.

When my father was appointed chief Resident Engineer for the rebuilding of the Wandsworth bridge in London we moved to number 10 Kingsmere Road near Wimbledon Common. The journey from Middlesborough for my mother, my sister and me could be described as "epic." We drove through appalling weather including the thickest pea-soup fog we had ever experienced. My sister Anne sat in the front passenger seat and spent most of the journey leaning out of the open window trying to read the signposts and asking pedestrians if we were still on the road to London. Notwithstanding, the trip was completed successfully and without major incident. I can remember the relief when we arrived at our new home, but it was also depressing. The house was without carpets and curtains and was cold and unwelcoming. Furthermore rats had taken up residence under the floorboards of this recently built dwelling. They were exterminated by the rat-catcher or rather by his ferrets which he set loose with freedom to carry out their grizzly task. This was accomplished within a few days. Bruno and his son Buster travelled to London by train and were tied up, muzzled, in the guards van. Our reunion with them when they arrived at Kings Cross station is etched on my memory. What a welcome we all gave each other!

Anne and I went to Oakhill School in Wimbledon until Hitler decided to disturb the peace with his punitive air assault. The Headmistress, school board and staff decided to evacuate all pupils who wished to leave Wimbledon and chose the south coast of England for relocation. After a few days a further move to Bedford took place. Two more moves were carried out before a satisfactory site was found for the school in the south of England. Anne and I were miserable and homesick and I was the only boy among some sixty girls, and perhaps surprisingly this was not acceptable to me! We therefore decided to send a letter to our parents requesting our immediate return home. This had the desired effect, our father responding immediately. He took off his jacket, took up a spade and dug a huge hole in the back garden of 10 Kingsmere Road. With the help of one or two workmen from the Wandsworth bridge site, an air raid shelter was constructed. The concrete was reinforced with steel mesh and the final result was a bunker of very considerable strength, certainly surpassing the "standard issue" Anderson shelter.

We used the air-raid shelter in the garden relatively infrequently. This was probably because my father had a somewhat fatalistic view having experienced several near misses during the First World War. He preferred to sleep in his own bed even though we were within range of hearing the huge ack-ack guns that were sited not far away on Wimbledon common. We were familiar with the drone of the engines of the German bombers as they passed overhead to destroy London. I recall the huge fire over the city's dockland during and after one of these air attacks. I stood in the entrance of the air-raid shelter looking east, the whole sky fiery red reminiscent of a majestic sunset painted by J M W Turner.

We must have lost a lot of sleep as a result of the constant barrage by the Luftwaffe that continued through the months of 1940 without relief. At the height of these attacks we would try to sleep squashed tightly into the cupboard underneath the stairs of the house. At other times we favoured the protection offered by the solid steel Morrison shelter that had been erected in the dining room. The "blackout" was observed strictly and we all carried our own gas masks in a square cardboard box that we slung over our shoulders. Large shelters had been built in the school grounds and we repaired to them when the sirens wailed their macabre warning threatening our safety yet again. One day I was walking on Wimbledon common with a friend. Suddenly we heard a droning sound that gradually increased in intensity. A great number of planes appeared in the sky with destructive intent. We learned later that this was one of the heaviest attacks the Germans had made on London.

We were spared from certain demise one night during an air raid when I was aware of a whistling noise that grew louder and louder. I could visualize a huge bomb plunging directly towards our home. It was without doubt destined to destroy us. I put my head under the pillow and an almighty explosion followed almost immediately. The house shook like a pack of cards but did not collapse. In the morning after I had dressed I went out to inspect the damage. The bomb had landed in the back garden of the house opposite ours. Fortunately the soil was heavy with clay and this must have absorbed some of the explosive force of the bomb. The back of the opposite house had been blown away and much of the garden was a huge crater. We were told that had the bomb struck the road between these two houses most of the dwellings in the road would have been razed to the ground.

One day I made a wooden bench for use in the shelter. One of the legs that had been split was repaired with a bracket for reinforcement.

I remember feeling quite pleased with my workmanship. But I was living in a fool's paradise. On my father's return home from work he asked me,

"What have you been doing today?"

I replied, "I've made a bench for the shelter."

"Let's go and have a look at it," he said.

We went through the kitchen and out to the workshop in the back garden. In silence he walked round my day's work and he must have noticed a split in one of the legs which I had cobbled together with a cross baton. He gave my bench a firm kick with his foot and the whole construction collapsed in a heap. He must have sensed my bitter disappointment and I felt that I had let him down in presenting such a shabby piece of workmanship. I was immensely impressed however by what he did next. He said,

"Now we'll make the bench together and I'll show you how to do it properly."

The task was completed satisfactorily and only then did he go back into the house for his eagerly awaited evening meal.

At about the same time he decided to build me a model railway for Christmas, still many months away. He must have worked some hundreds of hours, late into the night, in a workshop that had little heating. He made templates out of mahogany into which brass sleepers were inserted and brass rails were held in position so that the two could be soldered together. The circuit was the size of a ping pong table and included five points and a crossover. Electrification was by a third wire rail that ran along side the track. Each evening, when work was finished the emerging railway was put in the loft under blankets. I never told him that I used to have quick inspections to monitor progress when he was away at work! This was a splendid present from a remarkable man, engineer and father.

He was awarded the Telford medal that is given for the best paper presented to the Institute of Civil Engineers annually, not once, but twice.

He gave me relatively little advice during these early days. He pursued the highest standards in all that he did. He taught me by example. I remember two of his suggestions:

"If a job is worth doing, it's worth doing properly." Secondly,

"The only thing I'm going to say to you about choosing a career is, I hope it is something constructive and not destructive."

I trust he might have approved of my choice of career. In fact, I know he did, because I was launched as a consultant in cardio-thoracic surgery well before he died.

He lived to the substantial age of 82 years. Several times I told him,

"You've taught me more about surgery than have my teachers in that subject."

"Nonsense," he would reply, "I never could stand the sight of blood!"

What I was trying to tell him was that he taught me how to tackle a job properly. If unable to succeed, not to give up, but find an alternative solution to the problem. I think he would have been proud to know that his son was elected as President of The Society of Cardio Thoracic Surgeons of Great Britain and Ireland in 1993.

During the war years we had some harsh winters with temperatures well below freezing for several weeks at a time. The ponds and lakes on Wimbledon common were frozen with thick ice. Skating was safe. Many people took to the ice and enjoyed the exercise that this sport offers. It attracted children and adults and those who preferred to play ice hockey in small groups. I was immediately excited to learn a new skill and started off with skates of antique design. The metal blade was mounted between two supporting pieces of wood. They were strapped to your boots and lacked ankle support. My grandmother gave me a five pound note when she saw how much I was enjoying myself. I remember purchasing a pair of skating boots with skates attached in a shoe shop in Putney High Street. I also skated at Richmond ice rink and a small group of friends used to travel from Wimbledon common to the ice rink at Richmond. One of our group was Sir Russell Brock's daughter, Angela. A promising career in medicine was tragically cut short in the prime of her life. I lived almost round the corner from the Brock family and my sister and I were invited to parties there at Christmas time. During the war Russell Brock was pioneering cardiac surgery at Guy's Hospital in London. Little did I realise that I was to follow in the path of Brock and Holmes Sellors, two of Britain's great pioneers in chest surgery. My other contacts with the medical profession in the early war years were through my sister, Anne, who developed an infection in the mastoid region of her skull. This operation was performed by an ENT specialist, Mr Wilson, at the Middlesex Hospital, to drain an abscess that was threatening to infiltrate her brain. The deep cavity had to be dressed daily with extensive lengths of ribbon gauze using long-angled forceps. Mother replaced these dressings throughout our holiday on a farm near the Brecon Beacons, Wales. The long-angled forceps were sterilized in a saucepan of boiling water on the range in the farmhouse kitchen.

Anne was not a natural athlete and found ball games difficult. Because of her illness she was advised to take up horse riding and she became an experienced rider throughout the early years of her life. At one time when she was living in Edinburgh she owned her own horse, Clachan. Anne worked extremely hard and obtained excellent results in examinations that enabled her to enter St. Andrews University to study English. Soon after she started at St. Andrews I made an epic journey on my BSA motorbike from Catterick military camp, Yorkshire, where I was starting my national service in the Royal Signals. During November, in freezing conditions, a flying suit was my only protection as I sped over the open roads crossing Northumbria and The Scottish Borders. I was scheduled to spend the Saturday night with my mother's elder sister, aunt Margaret, who lived in the family house, Hopefield, in Edinburgh. I arrived on her doorstep almost unable to move, stiff as a board, through exposure to the severe conditions. I rang the bell with difficulty. Such was my appearance that she failed to recognise her nephew! She led me upstairs and soon had my feet in a bowl of piping hot water. The next day, Sunday, saw me crossing the Firth of Forth by ferry and keeping my promise to have lunch with my sister in "Hall" at the university. Almost immediately after lunch I remounted my machine and made the long journey back to camp. Mission completed!

Anne taught English for many years in southern England and in Edinburgh. She nursed our mother tirelessly during a terminal illness until she finally succumbed to cancer at the age of seventy two in 1964. My mother lost weight progressively. Her passing was mourned by many people. She was a selfless soul, giving herself unsparingly in the service of others. She was a fine example of the Christian way of life.

Auntie Margo had a hilarious sense of humour. She told me that one evening during the war she went downstairs to answer the front doorbell. She was confronted by a refugee from Poland who pleaded with her, in broken English, to take him in as a lodger. The conversation developed as follows: "I do not wish to eat with you, I do not wish to drink with you, I only wish to sleep with you." She told this amid gales of laughter and with a twinkle in her eye.

I found moving to the new property at 10 Kingsmere Road, with open ground behind it, somewhat depressing. However, with my father's practical skills and managerial organization, this situation improved fairly rapidly. He employed a part time gardener and had help from a number of skilled workmen such as bricklayers, a tiler, and an electrician. The single garage was an integral part of the house. The furthest part of the garage was built as a coal cellar and garden tool shed. The latter two parts were later knocked through and extended to create a double garage. The garden was a good size behind the house and a new building was erected providing a coal cellar and tool shed and a workshop area of approximately four hundred square feet. The strongly built greenhouse formed a continuation of the building, beyond this area. During the war when my mother and father ran a precision engineering business, part of the greenhouse was incorporated into the workshop to give much needed extra space. The equipment was of high quality and my father's old German lathe was augmented by the purchase of a five inch Atlas lathe and a slightly smaller but better quality South Bend lathe. A mechanical hack-saw and a small shaping machine were included. There were full sets of taps and dyes for cutting threads. All manner of hand tools were available and one learned something of the use of a micrometer and a Vernier scale. One of the tools I enjoyed using most was a pedestal drill that could be adapted for working wood or metal. This had the facility of a depth stop and mortise joints could be created by routing away the required wood. When the head of the machine had been fixed to the required depth the mortise was quickly created. My father was adept at cutting mortise and tenon joints and used his skill in building woodworking benches out of Oregon pine which had a beautiful smell of resin that one enjoyed when working this fine timber. He believed that every young boy should own a bench and a basic kit of tools so that he could develop his manual skills.

I therefore grew up in an environment of achievement, endeavour and challenge that equipped me for later life. I had the good fortune to come under the influence of the foreman and two other full time turners who treated me as a young apprentice in their chosen field of work. The foreman, Mr Ford, was lucky to survive an air raid one night when a bomb came very close to destroying his home. Perhaps he was accident prone or blessed by good fortune. He had an accident one day when he caught a finger in the lathe and he came running into our kitchen where mother was preparing supper. She examined this horrible wound and noted that the cut through the finger was clean. The distal portion of his finger had been severed apart from some skin attachment. Mother was good at bandaging and she approximated the lacerated pieces and drove him to the hospital. The follow up report indicated that the finger, in some miraculous way, had healed perfectly.

Much of my time was spent in the workshop and I learned to build wireless equipment under the guidance of one of the full time employees. My father used to attend when country mansions were being sold at auction. After one such occasion he returned home with a magnificent stationary steam engine. The boiler was coal fired and was approximately fifteen inches long and four inches in diameter. The chimney was about ten inches high and the fly-wheel some five and a half inches in diameter. Very small wooden sticks had to be cut to get the fire ignited and small pieces of coal were prepared in advance. Although this was great fun to play with, it was immobile and, clearly, as my second form of transport, required wheels! As I did not have access to a narrow gauge railway track I decided to make my steam engine pavement worthy! I designed and built a sub-frame that was mounted on four pram wheels. The front axle had a central pivot and the driver's feet steered the vehicle. The driving force was transmitted to the rear wheels through a "V" belt that connected the fly-wheel to a grooved pulley wheel that was attached to the rear axle. There were no brakes and no clutch. A low seat accommodated the driver, distributing his weight over the line of the rear axle. When steam was up, this puffing Billy could sprint along the pavement at a pleasing speed, certainly faster than walking pace. This vehicle would run as long as the driver had fuel prepared and water was available for conversion into steam. One day I was having a good run in my engine when a police car approached in the opposite direction. I became acutely anxious as I had neither vehicle licence nor insurance! I had not reached an age, being about ten or eleven years old, at which I could apply to drive lawnmowers, steam and traction engines and the like! To my immense relief the driver of the police car opened his window and gave me a salute accompanied by a broad smile.

One of the disadvantages of this mode of transport was that getting up full steam took time. This could be rectified to some extent by filling the boiler with very hot water. In an attempt to speed things up further, I decided to use my mother's vacuum cleaner to draw the draught through the boiler by applying suction to the open end of the chimney. Little did I imagine that I was to be responsible for starting a conflagration of major proportion as sparks were drawn from the fire box up through the chimney and into the bag of the vacuum-cleaner. The bag was consumed rapidly and I approached my mother in trepidation. Suffice it to say that she was not best pleased with this unnecessary catastrophe. This episode reminds me to acknowledge the support and encouragement that my parents gave me during these formative years.

However, my mother often despaired of my achieving the exams which her brothers had surmounted, enabling them to enter the medical profession. My mother's brother, Uncle Edward obtained his degree in medicine at Edinburgh University at such a premature age that he was obliged to wait more than a year before commencing his studies. She also told me that the examinations one needed to pass to become a fellow of the Royal Colleges of Surgeons were amongst the most difficult in the world. This remark was anything but encouraging to a young boy who was demonstrating practical skills and was definitely weak in mathematics and also struggled with Latin.

During my school years none of my teachers made sure that I was applying myself adequately to my academic work. It was not until I had completed two years doing National Service in the Royal Signals and I had entered medical school, that I began to study seriously. One of the arts of teaching is to ensure that students understand how to study rather than learning their work by rote. We shall return to this theme later.

It was necessary for the family to move from Yorkshire to Wimbledon because of my father's appointment as Resident Engineer for the replacement of the old stone bridge with a steel one across the River Thames at Wandsworth. During the construction of this bridge I learned about the way water is held back by caissons enabling the workforce to dig out the river bed until bed rock is exposed. The foundations of the bridge are then keyed into the rock. A caisson is something like a tin can that is opened at both ends. This tubular structure is towed out into the river by tugs before it is allowed to sink into the mud that forms the most superficial layer of the river bed. The mud and silt are dug away progressively, within the confines of the caisson, until bed rock is exposed and the granite foundation piers are anchored into the natural rock. The early part of this work may require investigation and supervision by underwater divers. Before modern equipment was available, these intrepid men took high risks as they could become affected by the depth of water causing pressure changes in their bodies. Some of them suffered from "the bends." This is a well recognized medical condition that affects divers if they are subjected to pressure change too rapidly. Bubbles of gas form in the blood and these may cause obstruction of small blood vessels in the cerebral circulation, with loss of consciousness.

My father was a sound sleeper and it was unheard of for him to wake up during the night. However, he awoke at about 2am on one occasion and was concerned that there was "trouble" at the bridge. He thought there might be a leek somewhere. My mother awoke to find him putting on his trousers over his pyjamas and he departed for the bridge site. When he returned a couple of hours later he reported that a dangerous situation had been avoided by early action. It seems that a major flood was avoided through a waking moment of intuition. The bridge was built out from either river bank. The day came when the union of these two spans was to be completed by the insertion of a central link to be towed out into the middle of the river by tugs. This event gained me a half day holiday from school. Those present were relieved and thrilled that the centre piece fitted into the gap with three quarters of an inch to spare. Expansion joints were incorporated in the bridge's structure to allow for movement due to temperature changes. The completion of the Wandsworth Bridge saw the end of the construction of any major bridge building in the British Isles until after the cessation of hostilities in 1945. My father's professional career as a civil engineer (in bridge building) was interrupted from about 1943 until 1956. He was recalled by his original employers, Mott, Hay and Anderson in 1956 to fill the post of Resident Engineer to the Forth Road Bridge in Scotland. I understand that the interview for his appointment lasted two minutes and one of his ambitions as a young man was at last to be realised.

A challenge greeted the Resident Engineer when he arrived on sight one day. A near gale force wind swept over the Firth of Forth. The power of the wind had started the north tower oscillating. Cables spinning had not yet commenced, leaving the tower naked to the elements. Men working on top of the swaying tower were beginning to suffer from motion sickness. Action was essential. Delay might have led to loss of lives and serious damage to the north tower seemed likely. An inclined plane or ramp was built on terra firma at some distance from the base of the tower. A huge block of concrete was constructed on the inclined slipway. Steel hawsers were attached to the tower half way up from ground level and to the concrete damping block. This had the desired braking effect and a major catastrophe was averted. I thought it was surgeons who had to deal with emergencies!

In the interim period my father was employed by the London County Council. He was involved in the reconstruction of roads, bridges and the like in and around London. One of his final tasks in the employment by the LCC was to ensure that the "Cutty Sark," the last of the clipper ships that sailed to and fro between England and Australia, was safely birthed in a purpose built dry dock at Greenwich. His Royal Highness Prince Philip performed the opening ceremony. The magnificent vessel was floated into the dock allowing this mighty seafarer to settle at her final birth.

I grew up with a natural enthusiasm for ball games. My sixth birthday party included a cricket match that was held in Wimbledon Park not far from the All England Tennis Club. The family and guests assembled and stumps were set. I remember the game quite clearly and talent for the game varied widely. The "naturals" did their stuff and enjoyed themselves whilst the "physically illiterate" suffered in contrast. I enjoyed handling a new leather cricket ball and soon became confident at catching. In later years I was a competent all rounder but more of that anon. I had a friend who lived a few doors away called Angus who batted left-handed. His father had been an oarsman in his youth and we cut short one of his oars to the length of a junior cricket bat. The ball used was a tennis ball and the stumps were replaced by a piece of wooden planking. The pitch was usually part of the concrete driveway at Angus' house. He and I would represent one of the famous Test elevens and we knew the players' names representing their country by heart. Hard fought matches were played regularly, one player batting until ten wickets had fallen. My father returned from work one evening to find me toiling for a very long time as wickets were hard to come by. Angus was older and physically larger than me and my father sensed that he had a considerable advantage. Dad said to Angus, "isn't it about time you gave David a chance to bat?" Angus who was well set in and who was enjoying himself thoroughly, replied,

"Oh, my father doesn't allow me to bowl!"

On other occasions I press-ganged my father into bowling to me as soon as he had returned from work. He was quite a useful bowler and needed some length for his run-up. To obtain this it was necessary for him to commence his run behind the chicken house angling sharply around this structure and avoiding the gooseberry bushes on the opposite side. Balls frequently flew over the fence into the neighbour's gardens and had to be retrieved either by walking to the front door of their houses and asking for permission or climbing the fence, hoping not to be seen. I enjoyed preparing a strip of grass, cutting and rolling it to create a better surface for batting. Years later I asked our groundsman at school, Bob Relph, how he prepared such beautiful wickets. He replied, "you have to get the worms working with you!" Occasionally the sound of tinkling glass was heard. On one glorious occasion my father was the culprit. The garden lawn was divided into two portions by a low hedge only twelve inches in height. I was practising chipping with a pitching iron. I was facing the house and was just about to chip the ball over the hedge towards the back of the house. "Hey, let me show you how to do it," said my Dad. Rather reluctantly I gave him the club. As he played the shot his head came up and the ball sped fast and sure and crashed straight through the sitting room window. I can see the look of disbelief on my father's face to this day.

One of my father's main hobbies was rough shooting. He was an excellent shot and he shared the rent of the rights to shoot over a small farm near Bedale when we lived near Middlesborough. He was hopeful that I might show enthusiasm and ability at this sport. This was not the case as I was not happy about wounding animals and birds and I had "no stomach for the fight." I accompanied him on one or two occasions with my bow and arrow and narrowly missed impaling a wood pigeon that was sitting in a nearby tree! My father was in great demand in the neighbourhood and folk would bring their problems to him, as spare parts for all things mechanical were difficult to obtain. Throughout the war years he ran a Morris Eight and acquired a second engine for this vehicle. I acted as his assistant over a weekend and we swapped the failing engine with the reconditioned one. We got this exercise down to about five hours of combined effort. His amazing knowledge concerning the fine-tuning of an engine was impressive. If the cylinders needed reboring he would borrow the specialist equipment tools that he required from a local garage in Wimbledon and he would carry out this task himself. He also decided to replace the petrol engine that was mounted in a Humber Snipe with a diesel counterpart. Diesel fuel was much cheaper and more readily available at this time. The exchange of engines necessitated repositioning of the gear lever and handbrake. The irony was that the Snipe became road worthy the very day that petrol rationing was discontinued! In the event, this large motor car vibrated like a London passenger transport bus and she was passed on in favour of a more conventional vehicle.

Anne and I cycled everywhere but frequent buses were available if needed. There was a strong sense of community in our district and most people took on extra responsibilities to help the war effort. Many adults became air-raid wardens and others attended first aid classes and other voluntary services. We cycled to school and back each day when we could assess the damage that the German Luftwaffe had created in our area. Pieces of parachute were caught in the trees fringing the main road. These parachutes were used to attack their targets by carrying oil bombs designed to start fires where they struck. The results of overnight bombing were to be seen everywhere. A family living in the next road from ours was thrown into the street by a direct hit with a large bomb. The two daughters were both killed. Friends of ours living close to this family woke up to find that they were surrounded by a huge pile of rubble. The small block of flats, including theirs, had sustained a direct hit. When my father and I went to the site in the morning we saw the full extent of the damage. We were able to retrieve some important papers such as passports, bank accounts and birth and insurance certificates. Hitler's intention to crack the spirit of the British people as a result of his repeated air attacks was a failure due to their defiance and determination. In fact, his aerial bombardments, rather than having their desired effect, drew the British public closer together than had ever been witnessed before .

Anne and David Hamilton

D.I.H. Golf on Wimbledon Common 1937

Ardneil House, West Kilbride, Ayrshire

Charles Blondin

SCHOOLING

I was fortunate to be accepted as a pupil at Kings College Junior School, Wimbledon in 1940. Thinking back over the key events of my life the way things turned out appear to me to be remarkable and require some explanation. My acceptance as a pupil at Kings College by Cecil Venner was one such event that could so easily have pointed me in an entirely different direction. Some would call it fate, but I prefer to think that God's hand was indicating the way He wanted me to go and I shall make reference to this throughout my mission. It is difficult to put the right emphasis on this aspect of my story and I hope to present my account of events truthfully, and hopefully, with at least a smattering of humility.

Kings College Junior School was founded as a separate Preparatory Department of the senior school in 1912. The first headmaster was Mr Bernard Wood-Hill and time proved that the governors could not "have made a more fortunate choice." Thanks to the devoted care of Cecil Venner, the Junior's second headmaster, the school came through the war relatively unscathed. However, the assembly hall was lost along with two form rooms and the recently built gymnasium. In 1945, the junior school opted for independence and increased its numbers to 300 boys. Every schoolboy and parent knows that a school is as good or as bad as the quality of its staff. Several teachers went to serve king and country in the armed forces. Temporary replacements were recruited to fill their places. Interruptions when the air raid sirens sounded became frequent and our studies suffered accordingly. In addition to our school books and gas masks, we each took a small tin box of emergency rations with us into the shelters that had been built in the school grounds.

My main memories of my time at Kings are related to the difficulties I had with the subjects of Mathematics and Latin. The latter was necessary for entry into Medical School. I had already set my sights on becoming a surgeon. My motivation for this decision stemmed from my father's ability to use his hands in wood and metal work and my mother's dedication as a nurse, theatre sister, midwife and missionary. The fact that two of her brothers became missionary surgeons in southern China had a powerful influence on me. The third brother ran his GP practice in Gullane, East Lothian, for forty years. My plan, as I entered the teenage period of my life was to combine all these skills within the life of a surgeon.

Cecil Venner interviewed me in his study when my mother was present to decide whether I was a suitable candidate to enter his school. Mother had coached me in general knowledge for weeks before the day of the interview. After a brief discussion he said, "Now I shall have to ask David some questions." Whether or not I answered any of them correctly, I cannot remember. One question, however, is etched forever in my mind. Because I had not started to read seriously, my spelling was lamentable. "How do you spell "talk,"" the headmaster asked. In a flash of enlightenment and relief on hearing this simple question (as I thought it to be), I replied, "TORK."

"How I wish it were so, David"

Turning to address my mother he said, "He's got a long way to go, but I'll take him, as I think he will make an upright citizen eventually."

I soon fell further behind in the subjects of Mathematics and Latin, in particular, but enjoyed History, Geography, English Literature and Poetry. Each and every boy had to learn and recite his chosen piece to the rest of the class when his turn came round. On one such occasion we decided to play a prank on our poetry teacher who from my memory, might well have been the Headmaster. One boy followed another with the opening line from The Funeral of Charles Woolfe, 1791-1823, "not a drum was heard, not a funeral note, as his course, to the rampart we hurried." The Headmaster's favourite poets were Matthew Arnold, Rupert Brooke, Walter de la Mare and James Elroy Flecker. His love and enthusiasm for the works of de la Mare return to me from time to time. Cecil Venner moved lightly through our lives. He was everyone's favourite, but never traded on it; and, for many, he provided revelation that has illuminated our lives, (KCJS Jubilee Magazine, p20, 1962).When we had tests, particularly in Mathematics and Latin, I would think up ways of "scrim-shanking" which amounted to persuading my mother that I was indisposed and not fit for school on a particular day. On one such occasion she came into my room to see why I was not getting dressed. I said I had a sore throat and possibly my temperature was raised. She brought the thermometer from the bathroom, put it in my mouth and went off downstairs to the kitchen. I used the moments of her absence rushing to the bathroom and placing the thermometer in running water from the hot tap. To my horror the mercury shot up to approximately 103F! At this point, I nearly panicked but held my nerve sufficiently to put the thermometer into the stream of cold water.

Mercifully the level fell to just below normal. By the time mother returned to my room the temperature recorded on the thermometer was still at this level. She packed me off to school not realising what had been going on behind her back!

The Headquarters of the American Air Force in Britain was sited in a large house and surrounding grounds just around the corner from our home. I obtained permission from one of their senior officers to make a cricket pitch and to practice basic skills with a rugby football. In return some of the American air crew taught me and my friends to throw and catch a rugby football in the American style. This entailed imparting spin on the ball to give increased length to the pass. Similar skills were practised with our feet kicking the ball with spin. Once, the ball landed in the flower bed near a large plant that had leaves of the succulent variety. The leaves were stiff and sharp at the tip. On bending down to retrieve the ball one of these long spear-like leaves damaged the white sclera of one of my eyes that became blood-shot. This injury earned me the next morning (a Saturday) off school. A telephone call came through during the course of that morning from the games master enquiring as to whether I could play in the afternoon match. By some extraordinary miracle I was feeling much better and no further bleeding had appeared in my eye. I therefore considered myself fit to play. Gaining my mothers' agreement was another matter altogether! I could not have done so had the match been arranged for the morning! In the event we won the encounter convincingly.

Sport was an important aspect of school life at Kings. For those showing average or above average ability there was first class coaching and encouragement to get selected for the various teams. This led to a number of players gaining the highest level in representative sport. I fell out with my piano teacher when I was about twelve because she realized that my playing was not "the first love in my life!" She was a first class teacher and I suspect she thought, quite rightly, that I was not practising sufficiently between lessons. I therefore terminated piano tuition that left me free to attend cricket nets during the summer months.

I surprised myself when I won the Victor Ludorum Cup for under 11's in the annual athletic competition. I pulled out an exceptional leap in the long jump that was unexpected. The cup was very large and it rested on the sideboard in our dining room throughout the ensuing twelve months. I was mad about cricket and my games with Angus Hewitt using a narrow cricket bat were designed to train our eyes to hit the ball in the middle of the bat. Don Bradman went further as he practised using a stump as a bat.

The sport that raised the greatest interest and support from spectators, parents and staff, however, was rugby football. Like Webb-Ellis I started with Association Football for a couple of seasons. Then we "took up the ball and ran with it" into an environment from which it was possible to achieve the highest honours. Two factors come into play here: the extent of the boys' skill, and the quality of the coaching staff.

In respect of the latter, the school was most fortunate in the appointment of Geoffrey de la Condamine as the number one coach to the first fifteen. Here was a man born to fill this role. He had played for Oxford University and the Harlequin Club as a talented scrum half before both his knees developed troubles from torn cartilages. This brought his active participation in the game to an abrupt halt. However, it turned him towards coaching which he took up with all the determination that would have marked his career as a player. Apart from developing a highly successful first team, each year a number of his protégés played for country, county and guest teams. Several went forward to captain KC senior school first fifteen or other schools at the same level. Thinking back and comparing the expertise of these youngsters with the International players of today, I can suggest why we were so successful at junior level: Geoffrey de la Codamine believed that boys of thirteen and fourteen years old could replicate the skill of their seniors when they were in their prime. We were taught the basic requirements for becoming top class rugby footballers. Members of staff were prepared to give up many hours of their valuable leisure time teaching the basics and travelling to and from midweek and weekend matches, all for the love of the job. Geoffrey de la Condamine was gifted in spotting talent before it had been fully developed. He was a skilled coach in teaching team tactics and in nurturing the art of positional play. This was achieved by playing short bursts of fifteen a side rugby using the whistle. The coach would blow it every few minutes whilst the training game was in progress and the players on both sides had to "freeze" like statues where they stood. He would then analyse the players' position on the field, using his own colourful language. At the team meeting, a couple of days after the last match, he would read out his critique of each team member. He pulled no punches but his comments were fair and respected. His enthusiasm for his role as first fifteen coach was infectious and moved from the practice field to inspire great play in matches. During the war years (1939-1945) the first fifteen played twenty seven matches against various schools. Twenty-five were won and two were lost. Seven hundred and seven points were scored against the opposition tally of fifty-five. He wrote in his book, "I am inclined to think that the school would have won anyhow and anywhere when players such as the following took the field: John and Richard (Ricky) Bartlett, G Mouatt, RR Winn, B Calvert, GJ Bendon, DI Hamilton, and VA Smith. Here we have a rich profusion of honours later gained from Club, University, County, Services, the coveted membership of the Barbarians and the final accolade of international caps. D Thompson played in an International trial match and full International caps were won by RM Bartlett and GJ Bendon for the England team. RH Davies played for Wales as vice captain. RF Camp of Guy's Hospital was selected by England to play Wales in one of the war time Internationals. DI Hamilton played for the English schoolboys versus France in 1949." Geoffrey de la Condamine's assistants in coaching were Frank Tomlins and later, Peter Gibbs.

I believe the secret of our success lay in the concentration on and mastery of basic skills such as the giving and taking of a pass with the rugby ball. This entails looking where you are passing and to whom, and straightening the line to avoid crowding out the wing three quarter. We practised tackling by hurling ourselves at a defenceless tackle bag that was suspended on a wooden frame. Other manoeuvres such as "change of pace," the swerve and the dummy pass were also encouraged.

We might have been prevented from embarking on our careers in rugby football had we not mounted a disciplined approach to Hitler's aerial bombardment of London and other great cities. Before each game, pieces of shrapnel that had fallen from the ack-ack shells that were fired from our own guns that were sited on Wimbledon Common were collected. The players walked abreast and quickly cleared these jagged metal fragments that could cause severe cuts.

At about this time it came to my ear that Geoffrey de la Condamine's birthday was approaching. As he was a pipe smoker, I decided to make him a cigarette lighter in the workshop at home. A local barber had the necessary "small parts" for sale in his shop. All I needed from him were a flint wheel, some flints and the spring to maintain tension through the flint onto the wheel. We had a hexagon-shaped piece of brass in the scrap box. I cut the brass into two pieces, one longer than the other. The longer piece was turned down on the lathe for approximately one centimetre. The shorter piece was bored out to form a cap that fitted over the first piece. The longer piece was to be filled with cotton wool moistened with fuel. A screw bung was inserted in the base. The flint wheel was mounted with a pin across a slot that I cut in a tubular piece of brass approximately four millimetres in diameter. This was passed through a hole that had been drilled in the upper end of the longer hexagon shaped piece and the wick was passed through a second hole close to the first. Apart from being rather heavy, it looked quite professional and worked very satisfactorily. I showed it to my father and to my delight he said, "we'll add it to the batch of work that's going off to be chromium plated." After this was completed the following week, it was returned looking like the real thing.

At the end of a lesson, I approached Condamine who was quite an intimidating figure, and presented him with the small package.

"What's this?" he said.

"It's a birthday present for you," I replied.

By now the package was open and he had taken the cap off the main barrel. "Where did you buy it?"

"I didn't buy it," I said.

"Where did you find it?"

"I didn't find it?"

"I hope you did not steal it."

"I didn't steal it," I replied, almost in tears, emotion beginning to get hold of me.

"Then where did it come from?" he asked.

"I made it for you!"

"David, I'm sorry, but I cannot believe that."

"Then I'll ask my mother to invite you to tea and I'll show you the workshop in our garden where I made it."

This invitation was forthcoming and I remember sitting round the tea table with my form master and rugby coach as our guest.

This occasion would have given my father an opportunity to comment about Condamine's suggestion that I might have stolen the cigarette lighter that I had made for him. What is more certain is that these two had a discussion that I understand became heated concerning the timing of my move to Leighton Park School, in Reading. My father had attended Bootham, the Quaker School in York, and he had planned that I should be educated during my teens at Leighton Park School. He decided that I should enter LPS in the autumn of 1944, when I was thirteen, but Condamine wanted me to stay at KCJS for another year. My father persisted and Condamine had to accept. Although he lost one promising scrum half, he soon found another in John List. Condamine wrote a splendid book, "Steps to first class Rugby," that was profusely illustrated. John List was the player who was pictured in the scrum half position. His career was relatively short as he joined the Navy and gave up playing. I became acutely anxious to find out which code of football was played at LPS. I perused the brochure that was sent out to would be pupils and their parents. Here I found photographs of the beautiful sixty acre park and ascertained that Thomas Hopkins was master-in charge of rugby, gymnastics, swimming and athletics (in the Spring term). "Hoppy," as he was known, had been an Olympic gymnast representing Wales. He played for Swansea at fly half but impressed the headmaster when he was interviewed for his possible appointment to the staff at LPS. Tea was taken with the headmaster and a few members of staff on the first floor balcony of School House. Hoppy walked on his hands along the balustrade. His appointment was fundamental to the school's development before, during and after the Second World War. In the Spring term virtually every boy had to turn out for athletics during each afternoon of the week. Hoppy, Richard Coleman and Leslie Scott were the main coaches.

Another major influence in my development whilst attending King's College was my introduction to "Crusaders." I remember the boy who asked me to go with him on a Sunday afternoon. Meetings were held in a flat overlooking the River Thames at Putney in south-west London. Classes were run by EP Olney, Frank Holding and Jack Hardwick. The Crusaders were a national group, interdenominational providing bible classes for boys and girls. After the Blitz the class moved to larger premises. The singing of choruses to Olney's piano accompaniment was an enjoyable part of each meeting and some of the words provide effective teaching to this day. During the summer months outings were organised from time to time and the game of puddox was played on Wimbledon Common. This was a cross between baseball and cricket. I attended one or two summer camps. As a result of this experience with the crusaders I wrote in the margin of my bible in 1941that I had asked our Maker to come into my life and to guide me through the ensuing years. This was in response to the scripture: Revelation chapter three verse twenty, which reads, "Behold, I stand at the door, and knock. If any man hear my voice, I will come into him and will sup with him and he with me." My basic faith and relationship with God has not changed since these early days. There are times when my walk in Jesus' footsteps has been meaningful and vital. But I have to admit that I have frequently strayed off the "straight and narrow" and have probably been selfish in following a star other than the one that settled over the stable in which Christ was born to us all. I became a member of the Presbyterian Church of England that later became the United Reformed Church. I was about eighteen years of age at this time. Up to then I had valued the tradition of the Quakers and still find their concept of the "inner light" to be appealing and helpful. To make time for silent worship during a busy life is of great value. I still attend Quaker Meeting from time to time, particularly when I am travelling. My prayer life has tended to consist of "arrow prayers" which are thoughts that come into one's mind spontaneously and on the spur of the moment. I used to pray for the safekeeping of patients who were to undergo surgery whilst I was scrubbing up in preparation for their operation. In 1995 I became an Elder in the URC at West Kirby, Wirral and in later years chaired the committee that held responsibility for maintaining the fabric of the church building.

Returning to the rugby football field I was influenced in wanting to play at scrum half by the exploits of one Ross Logan, who lived in the Border country and first played for Scotland as a nineteen year old. He remained as his country's scrum half throughout the nineteen thirties. Cathy was one of Ross Logan's two sisters. Both married my Uncle Harry as Cathy died prematurely of cancer but not before they had added five children to their family. Cathy's sister, Lil, married Ross Logan after Cathy's death, and there were no children in that union. Harry and Cathy's eldest son, John Kirk, won several caps for Scotland and also played for the army. He was in the winning Scottish team when they defeated a strong New Zealand XV that was equivalent to the famous "All Blacks." Jean, John's eldest sister qualified as a masseuse (physiotherapist) and married Dr Archie Sloan. They emigrated to Cape Town where Archie became professor of physiology. John qualified in medicine at Edinburgh University. He was in the winning team for the Army's inter-regimental cup. On that occasion the trophy was presented by Field Marshal Montgomery. I had cycled with my friend Tom Greeves from Leighton Park in Reading to Aldershot to watch this match. After the players had left the field for a hot bath, Monty was standing alone in the middle of the pitch. I decided to ask him for his autograph. As I stood in front of him I noticed that I was taller than him. He was neatly attired in battle dress and beret. In reply to my request for his autograph, he said,

"Why should I give you my autograph?"

"Because it would give me great pleasure as a happy memento of this great day."

"That's a good enough answer for me," he said, taking his pen from his pocket. He wrote across my programme "Montgomery of Alemaine." I have kept this memento safely to this day.

John's younger brother, Logan, captained Edinburgh University at rugby in 1957-58. Their sisters were Elizabeth who had a rich artistic gift and Catherine who married Dr Logan Blackett who ran a GP practice in Gullane, East Lothian, after my Uncle Harry's retirement.

Uncle Harry subsequently married Cathy's sister, Lil. The brother of these two delightful ladies, Ross Logan's early rugby training was at Merchiston School in Edinburgh. He was tough, brilliant in defence and devastating as an attacking player. He used an unusual form of the "dummy pass." A dummy is sold to an opponent when the player selling the dummy feigns to pass the ball to one of his colleagues but withdraws the ball back at the very last moment. The more realistically this is performed the more effective does it become in sending the would-be tackler towards the player who is expecting to receive the pass. This opens up a gap through which the holder of the ball can break, maintaining the attack at high speed. Ross' interpretation of this manoeuvre was unique as he favoured wafting the ball at face level rather than at the more usual waist level. Playing against

Wales in the 1930s Ross used the dummy to perfection pretending to carry out a reverse pass to his three-quarter line that "sent" the whole of the Welsh fifteen in the wrong direction whilst he crossed the line to score a try for Scotland without a hand being laid upon him.

Sadly whilst serving in France during the Second World War he trod on a land mine that detonated and damaged one of his feet severely. Never the less his wicket-keeping to a gifted bowler in the Border country was described as being the next best thing to Godfrey Evans, "standing up" to Alec Bedser, one of the Bedser twins who played for England.

Before the commencement of the 1943 rugby season at KCJS I knew that the first fifteen needed a scrum half to replace RM Bartlett (Ricky). He had moved on to Stowe School and was later awarded caps by Cambridge University and England. I determined to try to play myself into the team as his replacement. I therefore practised throwing out passes to a friend who acted as fly half. Condamine saw me doing this in the lunch break and asked me to repeat the feat. I duly gained my place in the first fifteen and spent some of my spare time learning to punt and drop kick a rugby football. I took to the game naturally and with enthusiasm. I can remember the first occasion when I used the dummy in a match against Whitgift School. I stole away from the base of the scrum in midfield selling a dummy or maybe two. The way opened up before me and I made twenty or thirty yards towards the opponents try line. I used the dummy throughout my career the majority of which was as a member of the Middlesex Hospital first fifteen over some eight seasons. I also played for London Scottish on occasion and for Berkshire and Surrey Counties intermittently.

My time at Kings terminated abruptly when I was thirteen years old. Flying bombs (unmanned aircraft) were Hitler's latest secret weapon that caused great anxiety throughout the civilian population. We counted thirteen in the sky whilst we were playing cricket one afternoon. The school was closed during the summer term due to damage inflicted upon some of the buildings.

My mother took Anne, my sister, and me to Edinburgh where we stayed at "Hopefield" her family home, then possessed by my mother's older sister, our aunt Margaret. The family house was near the Links at Bruntsfield and was situated at the junction of Greenhill Gardens and Chamberlain Road not far from Holy Corner. This gave us an opportunity to explore a fine city,

ARMY RUGBY UNION CHALLENGE CUP

Montgomery of Alamein F.M. (signature)

FINAL

2nd Bn. WELSH GUARDS

versus

DEPOT & TRAINING EST. R.A.M.C.

COMMAND CENTRAL GROUND
Queen's Avenue - Aldershot

FRIDAY, 25th APRIL, 1947
KICK-OFF 3 p.m.

GOD SAVE THE KING

PRICE - - - THREEPENCE

Wm. May & Co., Ltd., Aldershot.

Montgomery of Alamein

travelling by tram and "shank's pony." After a few weeks we moved to Gullane to more suitable lodgings near Fausetthill, the home of Dr HEB Kirk, my uncle Harry. He was a much-loved General Practitioner spending his whole life caring for and ministering to the people of East Lothian. For the humble fee of ten shillings I was able to play over Gullane's number one golf course throughout the summer. David Huish later professional at North Berwick was the assistant pro at Gullane at that time. We met again years later at Penina in Portugal spending a very happy evening with our wives and his lady caddy. He led the Open Championship for two rounds at one time and his low-trajectory driving, keeping the ball under the wind, was his trade mark. We enjoyed the encouragement he gave us when he came to run his eye over our swings on the practise ground the following morning.

My father joined the Royal Engineers as an instructional officer in the erection of the Bailey Bridge in Hampshire and in the construction of the Mulberry Harbour at Bewley. He obtained leave to accompany me from Scotland to enter Leighton Park School for the commencement of the Autumn term in 1944. We spent a miserable night at 10 Kingsmere Road, the house being cold, empty and unwelcoming. Next day we made the journey from Paddington to Reading on the Great Western Railway. My father hated "goodbyes." Our parting was brief and emotional.

Leighton Park School opened in 1890 with four pupils. The early development of the school was slow. Progress was made under Charles Evans, whose father had been headmaster of two Quaker schools, Sidcot, and Ackworth. Gradually, Leighton Park became accepted and with Bootham in York, became a major school for boys in England.

During my teens I played golf during the holidays but had little time for it over the ensuing years. When I was training at medical school, I always tried to take a day off before important examinations and leave London to play golf with a friend. This emptied my mind and insured that I approached the exam in as relaxed a state as possible. Leighton Park School provided a privileged and protected environment for its pupils, some of whom came from overseas where their parents or guardians were working. I appreciated the teaching of several members of the staff in particular. Two became long-standing friends after I left school in 1949. Richard Schardt, Biology master, par excellence lent me a radio when I was in the fourth form and was the only boy in the school to contract German Measles. I reported to the House Matron with a sore throat and, I thought, a fever. I was admitted to the hospice and spent some of the time listening to commentaries on the cricket Test matches by John Arlott, EW Swanton and others. My friendship with Ricky continued throughout his life. He was a regular member of the Falcons Cricket Tour that was based at Leominster and met for one week in August each year. The Falcons tour had a life span of 100 years and was enjoyed by many old boys, staff and senior pupils, the majority of whom had attended Quaker schools. Several of the team met in a particular bakery in Ludlow before the annual match with the Town. Coffee and sticky cake were consumed in large quantities and were a feature of the tour. Harold Broadbent was temporarily employed at LPS to teach biology in Richard Schardt's absence. He was a gifted sportsman and was welcome on tour. Few of us suspected, however, that he would clear an adjoining tennis court of players as a result of an 80 run aerial bombardment, endangering lives. The tennis players would only return to the court when Harold himself had repaired to the cricket pavilion. Harold took me pillion on his motorbike with our golf clubs from LPS to Sonning golf course when the school was given a half-day holiday for some reason. He was popular with the sixth form biology set when he brewed us cups of coffee, during a practical examination. Had the inspectors come on their rounds he was going to tell them that we were experimenting with a natural alkaloid.

Leslie Scott, an interesting personality, taught me Latin in the early part of my time at LPS. He was a good athlete and I appreciated his coaching on the tennis courts. He also introduced me to high hurdling at which I represented the school, and later, the Royal Signals in the Army Championships, held at Aldershot in 1951. Leslie enjoyed entertaining his class on days when important events were scheduled, some of which took place within the park or in the wider world. For example, we attended the Oxbridge rugby match at Twickenham. He would select a text at random and would then apply it to the event in question, skilfully anticipating the outcome. This process appealed to our youthful imaginations and we held him in high esteem. He came up with the statement in one class "you know that I was an undergraduate at Edinburgh University." Then he added, "I ran behind Eric Liddell" (the Scottish and Olympic runner who declined to race on a Sunday). I was sorely tempted, but lacked enough courage, to question,

"Yes, Sir, but how far behind?"

He left before I entered the Sixth form years to become headmaster of the City of Bath School.

Thomas Hopkins (Hoppy), Hilda and daughters Wendy and Gill, all fine athletes in their own right, were amongst the most ardent supporters of LPS athletics and rugby. Hoppy was also in charge of swimming and gymnastics. He made a visit to Denmark to study their approach to teaching gym before he was appointed to LPS. His influence spread throughout the school since every pupil came under his charge. When he was invigilating at examination time he insisted on all those present observing a three-minute period of silence before he started the clock ticking. Thomas Hopkins exhibited the finest characteristics of the Welsh. He was totally dedicated to his work being as interested in the spiritual side of his charges as much as he was in their physical development. His insistence on every pupil turning out for athletic training every afternoon in the spring term produced a number of first class athletes. One of these, Christopher Windle ran in the style of Sebastian Coe. He won the half mile at the public school athletic meeting in 1949. Hoppy nurtured a group of boys who had no idea that they might be capable of performing at the highest level. From a much smaller number of athletes Leighton Park beat Eton College twice in the five years I was at the school.

Richard Coleman ably assisted him in the organisation of athletics. Richard taught Classics, Divinity, and Ancient History from 1941 to 1971. I came under his care when he was in charge of the Colts rugby team and what a privilege it was to be carried along with this exceptionally fine man. His enthusiasm for life and achievement in everything he was involved in emanated from his deep faith. His eyes were clear and focused as he gave total concentration to the job in hand. His records and notes of Athletic events at LPS were kept beautifully in his characteristic handwriting. His expertise at pole vaulting drew boys into this event. Richard's life spoke of his beliefs. He lived it as he believed it should be lived. His gentle nature was a formative influence on everybody on the park. Frank Button and Victor Stables were members of staff who joined LPS during the war years and became part of the permanent structure in subsequent years.

I enjoyed my time at LPS as it was packed with activity according to the season; rugby in both winter terms and athletics taking over half way through the latter part of the spring term. Cricket and tennis were played in the longer summer term. Some boys concentrated on tennis and expert coaching was available under the inimitable eye of Herbert Brown, the Essex county coach who motored across London every Monday to LPS. He concentrated on developing sound footwork and swinging the racket, stroking the ball with top-spin and driving the ball to a full length. In 1949, immediately after the end of the summer term Leighton Park entered a team for the Youll Cup, the competition for public schools that was held at the All England Lawn Tennis Club, Wimbledon.

Quoting from the Leightonian Magazine of December 1949, we read:

"Public Schools Tennis Week for the Youll Cup.

Our team consisted of RW Sherborne, DI Hamilton, JB Bartlett and CG Palmer. It was unfortunate that DJ Ward and PW Phillips who had proved themselves to be in the same class as the others had to be left out of the team.

Our first match against Aldenham provided us with a shock as our first pair lost the second set against their first pair 10-12. Bartlett and Palmer won both their matches comfortably and we finally won, however, four matches to none.

Next came the best match of them all; Sherborne and Hamilton against the Eastbourne first pair. This was a well fought struggle right to the last point, the volleying was often brilliant and we were taken to three sets, the last being 9-7. Our second pair lost to this pair, but beat their second pair by accurate lobbing. We finally triumphed by three matches to one. We beat Brighton 4-0 and then faced Stowe, the previous year's finalists in the semi-final round. Sherborne and Hamilton against their first pair was the key match. After losing the first set we won the second easily and then, alas, lost the final set when we had been at match point and what might have been the final volley of the match, but the ball hit the net chord and fell back on our side of the court. We had lost the advantage and failed to regain it. Bartlett and Palmer made a gallant effort against the same pair, taking them to 6-8 in the second set. A deciding singles match, when Richard Sherborne represented LPS was lost one set to two. All four players played fine tennis and were chosen to play for the Public Schools team against the All England LTC on the Saturday but only Palmer was able to accept the invitation."

Sherborne and Hamilton disappeared to join the Falcons cricket tour based at Leominster. (Much of this report is taken from J Knox Taylor's description of the event.)

Another member of staff who became a lifelong friend was Kenneth F Nicholson. He taught me English in the sixth form. He was housemaster of School House and was in charge of the First Eleven cricket team. Kenneth and his brother, Harold, played for one of the well-known clubs in North London during the summer holidays. They were both impressive, stylish and effective batsmen and fine fielders. He captained the Falcons Tour and was delightful company since during this week friendships were cemented and the camaraderie between members of the Tour was fostered. We stayed in a house owned by a couple who were extremely hospitable and also fed us when we were hungry after the day's toil with superb meals. All the vegetables we ate were grown by Mr Ferguson in his large garden.

After one season playing rugby for the Colts under XV team I graduated to the second XV. I grew rapidly in height at this time reaching six foot on leaving school. This was uncommonly tall for a scrum half, but I was keen to maintain that position as I had developed an attacking game, frequently breaking from the base of the scrum to link up with the wing forwards and other members of the pack. David Pim, one of three Irish men in the unbeaten first school XV of 1949 was a naturally gifted performer who roamed menacingly over the field, devouring opponents in crunching tackles or cross-kicking from the wing into the centre of the field. He was unorthodox, had excellent hands and between us we scored approximately 30 tries during the season. David had played scrum half throughout the previous season. He was gracious in agreeing to move to the open side wing forward position that allowed me to play at scrum half.

My own game developed during these seasons at LPS. My right foot kicking was strong and I learned to impart spin on the ball, slicing it in contact with the boot and this achieved extra distance. Drop-kicking had been mastered at Kings College School and was used occasionally from open play and, once or twice, for long range penalty kicks.

Wednesday the 17th November 1948 was memorable for me. Hoppy came to find me and brought me the news that I had been selected to fill a gap in the Berkshire County XV which was playing Sussex at the Palmer Park Stadium in Reading that afternoon. Another seventeen year-old schoolboy,

Worsley (Reading School) filled the full back position. I was replacing the Harlequin scrum half, Austin Smith, who was unable to travel down from London at the last minute. The fly half was Owen Jones of London Welsh and he was a great source of strength to me during a game that Berkshire won by 23 points to 6. Later on I played several games for Berkshire and Surrey and London Scottish whilst playing regularly for Middlesex Hospital. One of the highlights of the unbeaten season, at LPS, was the annual game with Reading School. They had a much larger reservoir of players to draw on. Their reporter wrote the following, concerning the match of 1949:

"We appeared to have won the match when our fly half, Fullbrook, kicked a magnificent penalty goal from just inside the right touchline, giving Reading School a two point lead. The final whistle was expected at any moment. Tom Greeves for LP made a searing break up to our twenty-five yard line. A scrum developed and the referee spotted a Reading hand guiding the ball back towards his scrum half. This evoked a shrill blast from the referee and another penalty was awarded to LPS a few yards in field from the right hand touchline. Hamilton lined up the kick and gave LPS the victory as the ball sailed over the bar straight through the middle, equidistant between the posts. The final score was Leighton Park School,15, Reading School 14."

The Spring term brought possibly the stiffest challenge to our unbeaten record. Beaumont College had not been beaten since they lost to LPS the previous season. There was an argument as to where the game should be played and they insisted on playing "at home" as they were concerned about an outbreak of chicken pox. We agreed to play on the banks of the River Thames at Runnymeade and we used the coach trip to whip up fervour and passion. This match produced one of the most memorable encounters of my many seasons playing rugby. Richard Coleman wrote the following exciting account and the full text appeared in the Leightonian of March 1949.Excerpts are included as follows:

Match v Beaumont College, away, won 9-6

"Few matches that I have seen the school play stand out so vividly in my mind as this one, when we beat Beaumont by 9 points to 6. It was a game of fine opportunism, breathless excitement and above all, of tremendous tackling. The Beaumont team, also unbeaten, looked big and competent as they lined up for the start and so they proved to be. Yet hardly two minutes had passed when the ball came to Roffey, he sidestepped, ran, and passed to Pim who ran hard and fast to score. Beaumont soon rallied and their heavy forwards began to assert themselves at line-out and scrum. Then a long kick found Talbot in trouble on his own line; the ball went loose and Beaumont had scored, the half time score being 3-3.

For twenty minutes of the second half the Beaumont team put on tremendous pressure and repeatedly drove us back onto our own line. Indeed, one three quarter did run through for a try, but the whistle had gone. Then a big centre, minus one sleeve of his jersey shook off three defenders and scored an excellent try. But now it was our turn; Hamilton and Greeves kicked well and play moved into the Beaumont "25." Then from a set scrum we heeled and Greeves quickly and coolly dropped a goal, 6-6. We still pressed hard and it seemed as if Pim would score from a cross kick by Roffey, but he just failed to gather the ball. Could we get near enough to score again? Would Hamilton be able to bring off one of his famous dummies? Then from half way, Greeves made his best run of the match; he cut inwards and just failed to score. There was a scrum five yards from the line; we had the ball. Hamilton dummied, and then made for the line as if no one should stop him. And no one did. A grand try. What more can be said. The tackling of Hamilton, Greeves, Pearson and Pim remained a vivid memory. Hamilton surely played his best game for the school, being resourceful in attack and devastating in defence. All the team played worthily of the unbeaten record which they have had against schools this season, a record, which, from the determination of their players they seemed firmly resolved to keep."

At the end of Hoppy's write-up in the Leightonian of December 1949 of the unbeaten season he stated that there had been many fine, individual rugby players at LPS since 1930. Somehow the key aspect of team-work had been lacking and how often the final pass went missing. The gift we gave to Hoppy in preserving our record was a result of winning enough ball quickly from the hooker and loose scrum to the half backs who had a shrewd idea of how to process it. I wrote some thoughts about the unbeaten season at the request of Richard Coleman in the book that he edited, with others, about the first 100 years of the school. The points made included the following:

In the autumn term: points for 265, against 81.

This suggests a strong attack and a watertight defence. The reservoir of players being limited because of the small size of the school produced some inspired positional changes compared with the previous season. At least three forwards in the unbeaten team had appeared outside the scrum during the 1948 season. Three Irishmen brought virility and destructive tackling and I had the stimulus of the family connection, with Ross Logan to spur me on. The hooking of Charles Gillett was vital as the ball came to the scrum half cleanly and very quickly. He was a tower of strength in the loose and he could handle the ball expertly. The lost art of dribbling an oval ball was one of his fortes.

I am inclined to think that the influence Hoppy exercised over all pupils at LPS through swimming, athletics, gymnastics and rugby backed up by a deep knowledge of each boy's character was of fundamental importance to our success.

I wrote the following appreciation of him which was published in the Leightonian:

I can see him now, cycling through the leafy park, corduroy trousers and blazer, singing as he wended his way back to school from lunch at home, back to the work he loved. He educated a huge number of Leightonians, teaching them to know themselves, their physical and athletic potential, their zeal and self-respect. He nurtured their satisfaction and pride in athletic achievement.

He impressed and motivated his pupils as a result of his personal ability. The training that laid the foundation for his outstanding achievements at Leighton Park between 1930 and 1958 began as a boy and culminated as an Olympic gymnast in 1924. He impressed the Headmaster when he walked the full length of school house balcony balustrade on his hands before he was appointed. If the school was small, his knowledge of the physical and spiritual potential of the developing human body was great. He was a man of vision and his methods were revolutionary. His opportunity was unique as every boy in the school came under his influence in gymnastics, swimming, athletics and rugby. The professional standards of the gym competition and swimming sports left a lasting impression on one who was not gifted at either. He insisted that we all train for the bronze medallion in life saving. On the academic front, he organised School examinations efficiently and when invigilating he insisted on a few

40

moments of silence before the exam commenced. A moment of composure for he recognised that man is a spiritual creature. His insistence that every boy took part in athletic training every afternoon throughout the second half of the Easter term came as a shock to many. It drew out reserves that few thought they possessed and enabled him to challenge the might of Eton College at athletics. This reminded one of David's victory over Goliath as on March 30th 1946 Leighton Park beat Eton 44 to 37 points.

He was truly a man for all seasons with very special gifts. Richard Coleman wrote the following appreciation as a fellow member of staff:

"He was able to elicit from the boys skills they never knew they had, and to enthuse them with his own passionate interests. Boys who were underdogs who would run a mile from other masters, always found a sympathetic friend in him. He seemed to foster those Quaker qualities of strength without aggression and gentleness without weakness. He was interested in everyone on the Park. Not many men have understood Leighton Park so well or done so much for it."

Returning to the rugby team of 1948/9, Tom Greeves led by example with his fearless tackling, cricketer's hands and an astute knowledge of the tactics of the game.

I was thrilled to be selected for the English School's XV against the French schoolboys in April 1949. Following several inter county matches, a final trial was played at Kingsholm, Gloucester on Saturday 2nd April 1949. I was selected as reserve scrum half for the match against Wales, which was lost by 30 points to 3. I partnered Fullbrook (Reading School) who very nearly destroyed Leighton Park's unbeaten record with his magnificent penalty kick from just inside the touchline.

The game against the French was disappointing for me. Late in the first half, I broke from the scrum, and was stopped in my tracks by a French forward who hit me so hard with his shoulder that my right rectus femoris muscle was ruptured. This is an important thigh muscle of the quadriceps femoris group. Had we played the present day squad system, I would probably have been replaced by a reserve player. I hobbled through the second half. We lost this match by 9 points to 3. Neither our captain, Ted Woodward, nor I was pleased with my performance but this accounted for the realisation of my first ambition to play rugby at international level.

I was appointed as a prefect in the lower sixth year and was senior prefect for my final year. This created yet another diversion from personal study that I am sure suffered from the wealth of extra curricular activities I was allowed to pursue. Knox Taylor called me into his study when I was in the lower sixth form and reminded me of the importance of not neglecting "the books." In spite of this I was allowed to drop physics and some chemistry and how I imagined I would ever get to medical school remains a mystery. I also had failed to achieve a satisfactory level in Latin and the place that Richard Coleman had backed me for at Christ's College, Cambridge, went by the board. In later years when Richard Schardt, my excellent teacher in biology, during some of my time at LPS told me in answer to my query, "yes, you were educable!" It was only after completing two years of National Service when I entered the Middlesex Hospital medical school, that I began to understand how to study and the principles for this were laid out so clearly in Edgar Castle's small book, "Better Thinking."

Having piano lessons discontinued by my teacher in Wimbledon led me to take up the clarinet with Mr Orbinski. I played in the school orchestra and later, the Reading youth orchestra and made a fascinating tour with the latter to Achen, Dusseldorf, and Cologne in the summer of 1949. These cities had been reduced to piles of rubble because of the severe bombing raids of the Allied Forces. Populations were living in shacks made of temporary brickwork, timber and cardboard. In the early morning queues for bread and simple rations stretched away into the distance. Nevertheless we received a warm reception wherever we went. I was housed with a family who had three children. The father was a violinist and we played chamber music together round the piano.

Edgar B Castle was at the end of his twenty-year tenure as Headmaster of LPS. His term as Head was stamped with dignity, expansion and development in many areas and I was grateful for his vast experience. During my final year he handed over this responsibility to John Ounsted. He was not much more than ten years older than me and I liked to think that I was able to play a small part in introducing him to the running of day-to-day life of LPS as senior prefect. He surprised me on one occasion when we were having a weekly discussion about these matters in his study in Townson House. A group of some dozen young ladies, who were pupils at the Mount School in York, had arranged to stay at Leighton Park School for four or five days to study a Greek play that was part of their syllabus. This was being performed at one of the boy's schools in the district and their visit and stay at LPS caused comment and some excitement! The Head told me that new arrangements would have to be made, as the strike on the main railway between Reading and York was indeed a reality. In reporting this change of circumstance, John Ounsted said to me,

"What are you going to do with them?"

Did I detect the very slightest expression of panic in his voice and facial expression?

"You must go and work out a programme for them."

Up to that point I had not appreciated any particular problem in organising entertainment for these young ladies!

Cricket was the major summer sport at Leighton Park. Kenneth Nicholson was in charge of the first XI and we were fortunate to have the services of RR Relph. Bob was a very fine man and cricketer. He and his brother both played for England and it is reported that Bob's county captain asked him to take his place at the wicket towards the end of the day's play as night watchman on one occasion. Bob fulfilled this commission remaining at the crease until the end of the innings and keeping his captain in the pavilion throughout the following day. We did not have enough contact with this outstanding man as he was too busy maintaining the 60-acre park with minimal help.

He picked Peter May out as an eleven year-old Leighton Park boy before he went to Charterhouse School, for his final training as a future England captain.

I spent four years in the first XI at Leighton Park largely on the strength of my fielding. I had practised at Kings College on the catching cradle and became a useful reflex catcher anywhere close to the bat. I batted aggressively anywhere from number 3 to number 6 but must admit that impetuosity cost me my wicket far too frequently. I scored a century against Reading in a club match. I was able to turn an off-break and bowl an effective out-swinger. This enabled me to take a bunch of wickets in house matches but my best bowling performance was in my final season, playing against Exeter College, Oxford, playing at LPS on the 15th June 1949. Batting at number one I was caught out for 4 and the school only managed to scrape together a meagre total of 111 runs. Nevertheless atmospheric conditions were in favour of "swing" and we dismissed our opponents for 75 runs. My contribution was 8 wickets for 14 runs.

In the final match of the 1949 season against the old boys, a two innings affair, the old boys scored 216 in their first innings. The school replied with 276 for seven wickets declared, 121 was scored by DG Taylor, 65 by R Sherborne and 27 by Tom Greeves. The old boys scored 177 in their second innings, I took 5 wickets and J Roffey taking 4 wickets. The school required 118 runs to win the match. My contribution was 106, and the school won the match by 3 wickets.

I should acknowledge the fact that Tom Greeves who was vice captain for the 1948 season generously continued in that role the following year, allowing me to captain the side in 1949.

I shall always be grateful to my father for his insistence on sending me to Leighton Park School for a Quaker education. When I attended between 1944 and 1949 the Quaker influence was omnipresent in the Park. The older boys attended for worship at Reading Meeting House, walking the 3 miles to and from the meeting. Worship was held on the school premises for the juniors. A service was held on Sunday evenings with hymns and usually a guest speaker. This was held in Peckover Hall. Another opportunity for worship was that held between 9am and 9.45am on Thursday mornings. This meeting was wound up with a period of singing, most of the songs having an historical or nationalistic orientation. Another Quaker influence was the absence of corporal punishment, the rod being spared and the onus on sensible behaviour resting on the individual pupil's shoulders. One of the reasons that influenced my father's choice of school was the excellent facilities for hobbies under expert supervision from teachers who came in from the surrounding district. Expertise in woodwork, metalwork, bookbinding, artwork and fabrication of ornaments using plastic was provided. The standards of workmanship achieved, examples of which were on show at the annual exhibition, were remarkable. Concerts were given by the school orchestra and some of the more serious musicians were members of the Reading Youth Orchestra. The forestry group helped the permanent staff under Bob Relph to look after the trees and shrubs in the Park. The Quaker tradition was part of daily living encouraging self-discipline under the guidance of the "inner light" elsewhere interpreted as the working of the Holy Spirit within us. This philosophy surely gave the pupils of this school every opportunity for their development into creative adults.

1949. Berkshire 23 Sussex 3.
Senior County XV

1948-1949. Leighton Park School.
Unbeaten 1st XV

Bob Relph. England Cricketer.
Ground Manager at Leighton Park

Classics Teacher - Leslie Scott
with Tennis Coach, Herbert Brown

Thomas Hopkins.
Olympic Gymnast 1924

NATIONAL SERVICE

When I left Leighton Park School in the summer of 1949, I was called up to complete two years of National Service. This was mandatory for young men aged 18 years. I could have deferred this and gone straight to medical school and trained as a doctor, then completed my National Service afterwards. I could have served in the army for two years and then started the long haul of training to become a surgeon, a process that would take some 9 years. Two points occurred to me. First, the medical experience I would gain from my time in the services would be relatively limited. Secondly, it would be better to proceed from graduation as a medical student into the post graduate years of training that were going to be required to achieve the status of FRCS, without interruption. I decided upon the latter course. This decision was influenced in part by an invitation to join the Royal Signals by one of their rugby recruitment officers who was present at the England versus France schoolboy International, in Gloucester. The Royal Signals usually featured prominently in the army Cup encounters. Several of us who were in the England schools team accepted this invitation and were duly called into the Royal Signals. We had to report to Catterick garrison in Yorkshire.

I joined a large party of conscripts at King's Cross station, London. We were, of course, a complete mixture of young men from all walks of life and we were about to experience one of the most unpleasant few days of our lives. Arriving at Darlington station, we had our first experience of the "Corporal and Drill Sergeant." We were at their mercy and their language was colourful. Sentences were imaginative, cleverly constructed and frequently humorous. The dissection of a word and the insertion of four letter expletives matched the skill of a surgeon at the height of his ability. We disembarked from our transport at Catterick camp and no doubt were welcomed by one of the training officers. The memory that I shall never forget is of our visit to the Quarter Master stores to collect our personal kit. This was a protracted session, lasting late into the night when we were tired and disillusioned. Under such circumstances there is usually a ray of light relief from some ready "wit." For example, towards the end of our first week, we were lined up outside the gymnasium to await our turn for "jags." These were routine inoculations. One of our number from Liverpool came out from the gymnasium to where I was standing. He was clutching his upper arm with his hand and was swinging his upper limb from the shoulder fore and aft,

"it's the first six inches that's the worst," he informed me.

His acting was good but his humour was misplaced! The collection of personal kit was one of the most soul destroying few hours imaginable. A large white canvas kit bag gradually filled with items of clothing, trousers, battle dress, tunic, berets, vests and pants, shirts, tie, two pairs of boots, mess tin and cutlery formed the basis of our effects. The harrowing thing about this was that some of these objects were issued as "raw material" and needed some adjustment by the regimental tailors. The boots would require hours of "Bull" before they were ready to be worn and exhibited on the parade ground. At this stage, nothing seemed to fit and when we appeared for muster early the next morning in our uniform we looked a motley crew to be sure. It was some time in the small hours of the night when we returned to our allotted barrack-room under the eagle eye of the barrack room Corporal. In his introductory words to his "charges" he made it clear that he was neither mother nor fairy godmother to us. We could consult him at certain times of the day if we had genuine reason to want to do so.

Basic training lasted six weeks. This was devoted to "square bashing" in platoons of recruits learning to march in unison carrying rifles which were heavy and cumbersome, being relics of the 1914-1918 war. Sessions of gymnastics or drill were supervised by the physical trainers. These "gentlemen" were generally regarded by the recruits as sadistic. They tended to pick on the physically illiterate and often gave them the rough side of their tongue and, at worst, could be cruel and vindictive. In the barrack room were recruits from "'Uddesfield," "Bratford," and Leeds. We were a complete mixture. The lad in the next bed to mine was unable to read or write and I quite enjoyed acting as his scribe when he wanted to write to his girlfriend. One learned much from the conversation in the barrack room at night before weariness from the day's activities brought merciful release from the less pleasant aspects of service to King and Country.

You may wonder why a boy brought up as a Quaker with their tradition of pacifism found himself answering to the call of armed combat should this have become necessary. Important things were happening in my life at this time. I was influenced by my mother's decision to revert to church membership rather than continuing to support my father's attendance in Quaker meeting. She missed communion services and the music that accompanies church worship. Communion services are at the heart of Christian worship as meeting around the communion table and the partaking of the bread and wine bring us near to the death of Christ upon the cross. His broken body and flowing blood, when he was crucified, are represented by the broken bread and poured out wine. Such services are poignant reminders of Christ's love for us all and for his followers in particular. My mother, having been brought up in the church of Scotland, was also a violinist and pianist, decided to join the Presbyterian Church in England at Putney. The minister was Reverend Malcolm McAra. He lived in the Manse with his wife Marion and their two children Myra and Geoffrey. They were sixteen and fourteen years old respectively at this time. Mother was happy with her decision to revert to church membership and my sister Anne and I both decided to follow in her footsteps; we also became members of this church. In discussing pacifism with the reverend Malcolm McAra in his study he asked me a hypothetical question,

"What would you do if your wife and children were attacked physically? Would you not go to their rescue? You know you would."

At Christmas time 1948 my sister Anne and I held a party at our home near Wimbledon Common. Several families in the district did the same and a group of young people grew to know each other by participating in activities together throughout the year. A few days before our party was due to be held Anne told me that one of her girlfriends was unable to come. This created a dilemma as we needed equal numbers of boys and girls as part of the entertainment was to be dancing to the accompaniment of the gramophone. I suggested that we invite the minister's daughter from church as first reserve. This was the manner of our meeting 59 years ago. No doubt the short red dress that Myra wore on this occasion made its own impact, but it was her personality and beautifully shaped nose that bowled me over! I asked her to play golf at Wimbledon Park the next day. To my surprise and to hers also (subsequently confirmed) she proceeded to follow instructions and hit some remarkably good shots. This was understandable when she admitted that her father played to a handicap of eight. Playing with him years later one realised that he was consistency itself and it was tragic that he injured the nerve supply to his arm in a bicycle accident at a time when he would have enjoyed playing both golf and tennis with his children.

At the same time as I was called up into the army, Myra was attending a resident course in housekeeping at Pax Hill, the home of Lord and Lady Baden Powell, commissioners in the Boy scout and Girl guide organisations. I reasoned to myself that we were both away from our homes, were under strict discipline and at times felt miserable and lonely. I therefore started correspondence with Myra. Her letters in her neat handwriting brought great pleasure. Our friendship was slow to ripen as this daughter of the manse was shy and found conversation difficult.

She commenced training as a physiotherapist at St Mary's Hospital, Paddington. This was a short undertaking compared with the six years it took me to work my way through medical school after I was discharged from the army in August 1951. Myra qualified and became a MCSP (member of The Chartered Society of Physiotherapists) in 1952.

The winter of 1949-1950 was particularly severe. Our billets were at Richmond, North Yorkshire. We were housed in brick built barracks that had been condemned as unsuitable accommodation for recruits, but had not yet been demolished. The walls consisted of a single layer of bricks placed edge to edge forming a very narrow structure between us and the weather.

Heating was by wood and coal burning tubular stoves positioned in the centre of each barrack room. We were very cold at night and were compelled to wear our denim trousers and tunics over our pyjamas and great coats spread on top of us. These played the part of the modern day duvet. In rising from bed in the morning washing in cold water was often impossible as the pipes were frozen. One evening when we had run out of fuel, several of us set out with torches for the coal supply to the sergeant's mess. Those left behind broke down the wooden lockers to keep the fires burning. Our basic training continued in spite of the weather and we were occupied laying communication cables for the telephone system in use at that time. At some stage in this preliminary training programme, I was appointed as company cadet sergeant major. This brought with it some responsibility for the standard of turn out and drill of the cadets on the barrack square. Drilling a platoon of soldiers is a frightening experience for the person giving orders. It is necessary to imagine you are one of the platoon and you have to choose the correct command before the inevitable happens. This includes the men marching into the wall of the gymnasium that often forms one side of the barrack square. Or as was depicted in the magazine Punch, some sixty years ago, the young Subaltern is under instruction from the senior drill sergeant who is standing close by his pupil and is bawling into his ear, as the men march rapidly towards a sheer cliff,

"for gaw'd sake say something, sir, even if it's only goodbye!"

After making a number of enquiries about my situation with the rugby team it was agreed that I could proceed to war office selection board (WOSB) for officer training. My posting for this board examination was to Barton Stacey in Wiltshire. The process took about three days and was interesting and challenging. It consisted of aptitude tests, leadership skill, integration into a team and suitability to be labelled "officer material." I passed through this experience successfully and was duly posted from Catterick to Mons barracks, Aldershot. Here we came under the eagle eye of sergeant major Britain. He was a formidable character with a voice like a fog horn that carried clearly across the largest parade grounds in the country. During part of our passing-out parade some three months later he walked among the potential officers with the Adjutant. They stopped close by me for several minutes as we performed rifle exercises to the drum. It was an eye opener to have him as a guest at a passing out party that was held in one of the local hostelries. He exhibited a great sense of humour and a wide interest in life. His punch line became,

"you're idle, sir, idle on parade."

This remark was levelled at an officer cadet who was free wheeling on his bicycle through the barrack lines.

On return to the depot at Catterick we were interviewed concerning our future postings. On entering the room where the interview was held, I sat in a chair opposite a table and was confronted by a brigadier who seemed to hold my future in the palm of his hand.

"And where would you like to be posted?" he asked,

"I should like to go to Austria," I replied.

"And why do you wish to go there?" he asked.

"Because I understand they have a first class signals unit, and secondly, I have always wanted to ski,"

"I think we ought to be able to fix that up for you," he said.

Imagine my dismay when I heard a few days later that I had been posted to the Royal Signals depot regiment at Pocklington, Yorkshire. True to form I found out very soon afterwards that I was duty officer the first weekend following my arrival in the camp. It was also Christmas. This was to be my first Christmas away from home. In the event I was welcomed into the home of Captain Lowe and his family who were generously hospitable in making me feel welcome.

I was soon playing rugby for Pocklington, often as centre three quarter and usually on the winning side. Rugby was strong in this part of the country. Gerry Wood, a fellow recruit, had been a pupil at Pocklington School and was at this time playing for Yorkshire and England. If I did not play regularly for the Royal Corps of Signals I did represent them in the summer at tennis. The main event was the Army Championships held on grass courts at Aldershot. I also ran in the high hurdles competition and relay team. My appointment to the depot regiment was relatively unexciting and I found time to organise a sports day for all ranks. In the winter of 1950 I ran a rugby team, several of the players being new recruits to the game.

My work during the second year of National Service consisted largely of administrative duties. It was possible to obtain leave passes at weekends when I was not required for duty in the garrison. The winter months, particularly in London, were bedevilled by pea-soupers, these being thick smog which lodged in the throat and nasal passages. Trains running from the north of England were sometimes several hours behind schedule. Nevertheless, my father was invariably at King's Cross with his one and a half litre Riley to meet me. I was released from the Army a few weeks early so that I could commence studies at the Middlesex Hospital at the beginning of October. Just before demobilisation, I was promoted to the rank of lieutenant that came as a pleasing climax to my time in the Army.

Myra and I continued our friendship and we became engaged at Easter time 1954. Most of our courting took place in my cherished modes of transport, firstly a 1936 Austin 7 followed by an exciting car for a student to own, a 1936 Lagonda Rapier. This magnificent car was one of some 250 of this model to be produced at Staines, West of London. The acquisition of the

Austin 7 was unusual. I had purchased a Matchless motorbike from the barrack room corporal at Catterick for £30 during my period of basic training. This proved to be a disaster as my father had predicted. He had been a motorcycle enthusiast during his post war student days at Edinburgh University. He used to strip bikes down in his father's conservatory, rebuild them, and make a small profit. The story goes that he was riding a motorbike through London passing westward into Hammersmith. A young policeman apprehended my father who claimed he was disturbing the peace in the neighbourhood. This officer had intended to charge my father. His machine was lacking an exhaust pipe, thus creating the racket. A lengthy conversation ensued, my father finishing triumphantly by selling the said bike to the policeman. Not surprisingly, my mother was on tenterhooks whist I was the owner of a motorbike. As a nurse she had seen enough accident cases, some fatal. Nevertheless she knew when she was beaten and she helped me in the purchase of a BSA machine. I enjoyed the use of this reliable, though underpowered bike until I was able to purchase a four-wheeled vehicle. The possibility to do this came as a thunderbolt and an act of God. On returning from our annual holiday in France I opened the garage door and there was a 1936 Austin 7 that belonged to my father's bank manager. Dad had given him permission to leave his car under cover in our garage whilst we went on our holiday. With eager support from my mother I persuaded my father to purchase it for £70. I used this "bone-shaker" for daily transport between Wimbledon and the Middlesex Hospital that was situated not far from Oxford Circus. As the first year of study in basic sciences at the Middlesex was divided over three terms, three generous holiday breaks intervened. By this time my father's business in precision engineering had been moved from our garden in Wimbledon to more suitable premises in Kensington. I used one of these vacations to strip the Austin down to its chassis and to reassemble it replacing any parts that were worn out. Soon after the Austin was back on the road I sold her for £170. This was just before my 21st birthday. My father came home one evening bringing with him a copy of the evening Standard. He said,

"There's an advert here that might interest you."

This advert described a splendid little car, four-seater, open-tourer, 12 horsepower. The centre of gravity was low and she held the road like a limpet. The Wilson pre-selector gear box enabled the driver to execute changes in gear rapidly and made the car competitive in traffic. The performance of the Lagonda was spectacular and she served me well for six years throughout my medical studies. The enjoyment was shared by team mates and friends when we made our annual tours to the West country for cricket and all over London and the Midlands during the winter months for rugby. Myra and I had a memorable holiday travelling through France, Austria, Northern Italy and back into France on our way home. This two week holiday together, unchaperoned, raised a number of eyebrows including those of our parents. The Lagonda proved her worth throughout the two thousand mile journey including some tortuous mountain climbing. The only minor problem we had with the car was that we ran out of petrol in the hills outside a village in North Italy. We were able to free wheel down hill to the single handled petrol pump. To our horror, the entire village had disappeared to the fete in the local town. There was no-one to draw fuel for us and, in addition, the winding handle had been removed. Not to be thwarted, I walked round to the back of the building and found a shed. There on the wall carefully concealed with cobwebs was the reserve handle we so desperately needed. I wound several litres of fuel into the Lagonda and left a note in French with some Italian Lire that was passed under the back door of the property. We were soon on our way, the engine ticking over as sweetly as previously.

We were driving in Northern Italy, South West of the Dolomites when we became involved with a cyclist. We were driving on the right hand side of the road and he was in front of us on the inside. Well in front of us, a factory with tall chimneys could be seen off the road to the left. The cyclist appeared to be a worker at the factory as he looked at us following behind him several times. He put out his left hand, indicating that he was about to cross our path, and then to pass through the open factory gates. Although I watched him carefully, it was not clear whether he was going to wait until we passed or whether he was going to cut in front of us. He made one false start, but lacked courage and cut back onto the inside position of the road. I therefore accelerated somewhat but at the same time he cut right across in front of us and he was picked off his bicycle cleanly and finished up sitting on the inside wing of the car, his legs still pedalling the air. It was not long before he fell off the car and he rolled into the rocky ground to the right of the road. A small crowd gathered quickly, some of them becoming aggressive towards us in view of the sad abject state of his machine that lay severely damaged in the ditch beside him. The front wheel had been pushed back so that it did not clear the frame of the bicycle that would then probably be judged a write-off. The man was "shaken rather than stirred" and we were fortunate to escape before the local police arrived on the scene.

The Lagonda provided transport for some students who came on the Devonshire cricket tour from the Middlesex Hospital annually. One, two or three passengers with cricket gear was a stringent test for the little car. But she would cruise at 60 mph all day if necessary. She really came into her own when the Wilson pre-selector gearbox was used, enabling the driver to keep both hands on the steering wheel whilst entering a sharp bend. This is best illustrated by an incident that occurred while we were driving from the hotel in Torquay to a small village, Cheriton Fitzpaine. We were in the middle of cider apple growing country. The lane was narrow with high hedges on either side as I remembered from previous years. Driving immediately behind me in his Ford Prefect was AD Jose, making his first visit on the tour. Tony was a very fine cricketer, an Oxford blue and an interstate quick bowler in his native Australia. He was completely unaware of the right angled bend we were about to negotiate. Changing down to third gear with little loss of speed, the Lagonda shot round the acute bend effortlessly. Tony, however, had no alternative but to continue into the farmyard where the resident chickens reacted angrily to this sudden intrusion.

My third boyhood ambition, to marry the right girl, was certainly not of less importance than the two other ambitions. During teenage years one gains an impression of the qualities one is looking for in the opposite sex as one's understanding of human nature grows. I believe that a sound and durable marriage is based on friendship and mutual respect. It is preferable that the couple have several interests in common and that they share a similar approach to religion whether that is meaningful to them or not. A love for music, sport, reading, or theatre are all fields where a couple can share their lives together. Following National Service, I entered medical school in the Autumn of 1952 and faced a daunting programme of study and examinations. Myra had already completed the majority of her physiotherapy training at St. Mary's hospital, Paddington. On qualification she was appointed as physiotherapist at the West Middlesex Hospital but later transferred to the Middlesex Hospital, whilst I was a student there. I set myself a stiff programme of study and apportioned the hours of the week to book work and practical medical studies. This kept Saturday afternoons free for rugby and cricket. The evenings during the week were spent in my room at 10 Kingsmere Road, Wimbledon Common. "Bashing the books" became a regular discipline until about 10pm. I attended practical classes, lectures and seminars whenever possible. Through the rugby and cricket clubs I was in touch with senior students and I used to pick their brains about the course and its demands and standards required.

The bond between Myra and me strengthened throughout my undergraduate training at The Middlesex. She exhibited much talent and potential ability in a wide field of activities. She acted as Akela to a pack of 30 cubs through her father's church in Putney. The long engagement until I graduated in the autumn of 1957 was stressful, particularly for Myra. My sights were set no further ahead than qualifying in medicine and surgery and later becoming FRCS, London. The fact that I finished up as a predominately paediatric cardiac surgeon meant that a great majority of my patients required a period of nursing and after care in the intensive care unit. This meant that I was on call for emergencies almost all the time. For many years I was the only consultant surgeon doing this work at the Royal Liverpool Children's Hospital.

Although I had read professor Ian Aird's book "The making of a surgeon," in which he makes this statement, "knife before wife," this did not cause me to think about this problem as seriously as it warranted. The life that a surgeon's wife is called upon to undertake is far from easy and extremely demanding. The fact that her husband is not available to help her in the home in times of need puts her in a position of home-maker, mother and organizer of family life to a greater extent than she would have envisaged. I have been fortunate in the stability of our relationship and our Golden Wedding has now been celebrated. There is a fundamental difference between leaving one's house in the morning to go to work when all is well and having to part when the relationship has not been good and dissension is in the air. The advice we were given by the minister during our marriage service, "never let the sun go down on your wrath," has not always been achieved. I am grateful to Myra for the quality of support that she has given me throughout my thirty-six years of hospital service.

MEDICAL SCHOOL

The Middlesex hospital was founded in 1745 as the Middlesex Infirmary in Windmill Street off Tottenham Court Road. Within a year teaching in the wards had begun. The hospital moved to a new site in Mortimer Street in 1757. Teaching received great prominence when Sir Charles Bell, proprietor of the famous School of Anatomy, in Great Windmill Street, was appointed as the first surgeon on the Honorary staff in 1814. Later he was appointed as Professor of surgery in the newly established University of London in 1828. It is interesting to record in the light of recent events regarding the amalgamation of the Middlesex and University College Hospitals on the Gower Street site was one of the original proposals. This would have developed a complete unit for a medical school, however it was decided that the Middlesex Hospital should have its own Medical School. Sir Charles Bell organized the building of such an establishment that included facilities for anatomy, physiology, biochemistry, physics, chemistry and biology. This work was completed in 1835. These developments were vital to the achievement of my own ambition as there were very few places offering a First MB course in 1951. In this respect the Middlesex Medical School offered me a tenuous lifeline, but one that was gladly accepted.

In 1856 the first Dean was elected. I graduated one hundred and one years later. My thanks go back to Sir Charles Bell for the effort he and his colleagues put into a highly successful project. The physical environment of the school was developed throughout the nineteenth century. This was made possible through the generosity of benefactors such as Sir John Bland Sutton, a surgeon on the staff who built the Institute of Pathology that developed a reputation for excellence all over the world.

During my period of National Service, I had given much thought to my future career. My achievement at A Level was not adequate to secure me a place that I had been offered at Christ College, Cambridge. I went through a period of uncertainty and made a request to the principal of the College to study agriculture or forestry. These were not my first options and were ones that would not satisfy me, because I felt that I should be working amongst people who were less fortunate than myself. I repeatedly returned to thinking that to achieve any role that is really worthwhile would mean a good deal of hard work and disciplined application. I also realized that if

God was calling me to be a surgeon He would give me the necessary mental and manual dexterity to achieve this. I called on my uncle, Professor John Kirk to advise me. I obtained a place at The Middlesex, with his support, and the day had arrived at last for me to commence a great saga that spanned the next twelve years. My first year at medical school included studying the basic sciences of biology, physics and biochemistry. The year was divided into three terms with generous holidays intervening. I used these breaks for rebuilding the Austin 7 in my father's newly acquired premises in Kensington Square. I signed up for the hospital rugby club and was promoted to the first XV after a couple of games in the A team. I occupied the position of scrum half for the next six seasons during which time the standard of rugby throughout the teaching hospitals in London probably declined from its highly competitive post war level. Hospital rugby was strong after the war by virtue of ex servicemen, some of whom became "permanent" students, and long-standing members of the rugby teams. Players of international status were regular members of the leading hospital teams. As these players graduated and moved on after their eventual qualification they were replaced by younger players who had come straight from school at eighteen years of age. My first game for the hospital first XV was against London Irish with DC Shields and CV Foll, who played in the second row of the scrum. The ball came whistling out of the scrum faster than I had previously experienced. Christopher Hopkins was a strong player from Ampleforth School at fly half. The wing three-quarters were JCM Wilkinson, an Olympic sprinter, and AD Jose an outstanding first class cricketer. In spite of frequent use of the "Garry Owen," we pulled off a famous victory. I managed to steal from a scrum, scoring a try near the corner flag. We played all the first class Midland clubs including Leicester, Bedford, Northampton, Nottingham and Rugby. As these teams became too strong for us we suffered many humiliating defeats. Our main endeavour was during the inter hospital cup matches played at Richmond Athletic Ground. These matches were fast and furious, no quarter being given by either side. Two other players who gave long service to the first XV were Peter Dale, who played for Halifax, and GV Lewis a Welshman who converted from centre three-quarter to open-side wing forward in his last two seasons. Peter's hooking was the foundation of much of our attacking play and Gwyn Lewis' tackling was outstanding.

I was less successful as a player in cricket although I played fairly regularly on Saturdays for the first XI and scored a match winning 86 against St

Bartholomew's Hospital at Chiselhurst. Based on exceptional pace from AD Jose and accurate spin from R Snelling not to mention Peter Bodkin's all round class which brought him a blue at Cambridge, we won the inter hospital cricket cup twice during my time in the team. As I declined to play on Sundays I lost my place and was not included in either cup winning team.

During one of the early summer breaks I asked two fellow students to accompany me on a tour round Brittany in the Lagonda. Our idea was to stay in youth hostels as our journey unfolded. Jeremy Parton turned up in Khaki army shorts and shirt, knee length socks and beautifully polished brown shoes. He portrayed the classic Englishman on holiday. By contrast Dennis Walters was a classical scholar to the Middlesex from Mauritius and was French speaking. He was a relaxed character who found studying in a foreign language difficult in the first six months of the first MB course. He seriously considered relocating his studies to Paris but we persuaded him to stay.

In Brittany we soon found that the accommodation offered in youth hostels was very basic and I had the idea of requesting a room at a major hospital in one of the large towns that we visited on a rearranged schedule. These included Saint Marlow, Bireuc, Morlaix, Brest, Douarnanais and Lamant. Some of these hospitals had trained medical students but some had not. One of these was run by nuns who were loathe to help us but Dennis' charm won the day and we were offered a private ward of four beds on the strict understanding that we left the building before the consultants 9.00am ward round. In spite of our best intentions we slept in and awoke to find the consultant with his full entourage of nurses and junior doctors standing in the room asking who these new patients were!

"Nous sommes etudians de medicine au Londres, monsieur?" Dennis was tested to the utmost but managed to talk us out of our dilemma without any real ill-feeling. At another hospital that catered for medical students no sleeping accommodation was available. Our dilemma had been appreciated by "Le Petit." He was handyman to the medical students. I noted his intelligence and summoned Dennis to discuss Le Petit's plan for our night's lodging. He accompanied us in the Lagonda out of town and some twenty miles into the countryside to a relative's farmhouse. We were soon fed and shown to our quarters in a spacious hay loft where we had an excellent nights sleep. We felt like French resistance workers being smuggled from one place to another under the noses of the occupying forces.

The holiday was a most enjoyable break from our studies and bound the three of us together in friendship. Dennis stayed in London and married a nurse from Germany and became a gynaecologist in Canada. Jeremy Parton, after graduation, was appointed as a houseman at the Middlesex. One day he heard the strains of a well-known hymn tune emanating from a linen cupboard on his ward. He felt constrained to explore this sound further. He opened the door to find one of the nurses attending to the contents of the cupboard and a friendship was established which led to matrimony.

Having negotiated the first MB exam successfully we were next confronted with the second MB course consisting of studies in anatomy, physiology, therapeutics (pharmacology), and biochemistry. In anatomy the students in my year were split into small groups for dissection of the entire human body, our progress being monitored by viva voce tests given by the staff of the department on a monthly basis. The teaching of anatomy at the Middlesex was of a very high standard. My uncle, Professor John Kirk had spent twenty years as a missionary surgeon in South China. He maintained his interest in the subject throughout this time and he supported his wife, a nurse from Birmingham, in establishing the first nurse-training school in southern China. On returning to London when his two sons, Jim and John, entered Mill Hill School, he was appointed senior Reader in anatomy at University College Hospital in London. He was later appointed as professor at Middlesex. Students spent many hours dissecting the human body. Cadavers were precious and hard to obtain as the following incident illustrates. Professor Walls who succeeded Professor Kirk came into the dissecting room one afternoon. He asked the whole class if any student had private transport that would enable them to collect a lower limb that was to be amputated the next day at the Central Middlesex Hospital at Acton. At this time no student could offer ownership of a car. I spoke up and said that I had a motorbike and would be prepared to collect the limb provided someone would ride pillion carrying the leg under their arm. The Professor accepted this offer with enthusiasm and designated the task of accompanying me, to Les, one of the technicians in the department. Our journey to Acton and back was unremarkable but I have wondered many times since how the police would have solved the mystery, had there been a serious accident, of finding an extra limb at the scene.

Fifteen months later, on the day we were to be examined for the anatomy part of the second MB exams Professor Walls was waiting for the visiting examining Professor, Sir Solly Zuckermann, who was travelling from Birmingham. He was also a scientific advisor to the government. Prof Walls suggested to Les, a cockney, that he should wait at the top of the stairs and should lead him to the dissecting room so that examination of students could commence. Les was also waiting for the male model who was to be available to display his musculature if the professors decided to question some of the students in this part of the curriculum. A few minutes after Les had positioned himself strategically, as requested, a somewhat dishevelled figure dressed in a brown mackintosh and with longish hair arrived on the scene somewhat breathless. Les made an impulsive assessment and decided that this was his surface anatomy model. He pulled out a pair of bathing trunks which he had hidden under his white coat and thrust these into Sir Solly's chest! At the same time Les opened the door of a deep cupboard and pushed the unfortunate professor into its darkness, saying,

"Get stripped off, the Professor's waiting for you to start the examination."

The story finishes with the statement that not many students passed their examination that afternoon.

Second MB is a tough examination. The factual content of the course is immense. Human anatomy was studied in great detail and similar attention was required in studying physiology, that is the working of the human body. Also included in the course was a study of pharmacology and biochemistry. At this time all of these subjects were included in the second MB examinations. I passed all parts apart from pharmacology and along with three of four other students was prevented from proceeding into the hospital for studies in clinical medicine that we all looked forward to eagerly. A new rule came into play for the first time that stated that we must pass the exam in pharmacology and we could not re-sit it until the following summer, i.e. one year later. Previous to this new edict students were permitted to proceed into clinical studies and re-sit it in three months. I was very upset by this but as it was the only exam including the primary and final parts of the FRCS (Fellowship of the Royal College of Surgeons) that I failed to pass at the first attempt I came through the whole course well satisfied. The fellowship exams are a real stumbling block to many students in surgery. I was in the Royal College of Surgeons in London recently and was talking to the concierge and was telling him of my happy memories of the evening when the list of successful candidates at the final examination was pinned to one of the pillars in the foyer of the College. The melee of students pressed forward scanning the list of successful candidates that was quite short. I could not believe my eyes when I saw that my name was included. I felt a tap on my shoulder from behind. An Indian doctor seemed to know my name as he said to me,

"Mr Hamilton, you are amongst the elite. I was in Glasgow when you passed the primary Fellowship exam at the first attempt."

I was most impressed that this potential surgeon was so aware of things going on around him. The concierge on hearing this story recently said to me,

"You are one of the one percent to achieve this feat."

I enjoyed studying anatomy in particular and was fortunate to have second choice of my uncle John Kirk's specialist books when he died in 1952. It was a privilege to study from his books, many of which had been donated to him by the publishers. His son, John Kirk had first choice of these when his father died and he became consultant plastic surgeon in Perth and Bridge of Earn, Scotland. He had a distinguished career and his work was held in high esteem by the local Medical and Lay communities.

This extra year gave me something of a break after the intense studying leading up to the second MB exam. It was a great relief to pass the pharmacology exam at the second attempt.

I now joined the students who were one year behind me originally in our quest for knowledge in clinical (at the bedside) medicine and surgery. This was a three-year course. The first part of the course was an introduction to clinical medicine based on lectures and demonstrations in bedside methods. This includes the taking of a medical history, the clinical examination of the patient, laboratory tests and their interpretation. Studies in radiology and special techniques, for instance angiography, and specialist investigations in cardiology are further examples of the far ranging curriculum. We were divided into "firms" of eight to ten students, each firm being attached to consultants in general medicine and surgery for three-month periods. My first appointment was to Dr Richard Asher at the Central Middlesex hospital, Park Royal, North London. He was a very experienced physician with a special interest in Psychiatric medicine. He was also the father of Jane Asher, the actress. He was a fine teacher and his wards were full of interesting patients that gave us valuable insight into general medical conditions such as pneumonia, bronchitis, bacterial endocarditis and rheumatic fever for example. He also ran an "obesity" clinic. I was sitting behind him with three other students at one of these clinics. The door opened and a very large lady was shown to a chair across the table from Dr Asher.

"Well, Nelly," as he perused her weight chart, "you haven't lost enough weight this month, have you?"

She cast her eyes to the floor,

"No, no, I'm sorry, Dr Asher."

"Tell these young doctors behind me what your husband does."

"He runs a fish and chip shop."

"Well, you must have been eating some of the fish!"

"No, no I've promised you Dr Asher, I'm never going to eat the fish."

"So you must have been eating the chips, Nelly!"

"Oh, no, no, we've agreed that I mustn't touch the chips."

"Well, what about the crinkly bits that fall underneath the grill?"

"Oh, yes, Dr Asher, you know I can't resist those."

My second three-month appointment was to one of the surgical firms, again at the Central Middlesex Hospital. The two consultants were Mr Ferguson and Mr Gummer. The senior registrar was Peter F Jones known affectionately as "Puffy." He had qualified at St Bartholomew's Hospital and was nearing a permanent appointment as a consultant surgeon. Because of summer holidays and shortage of junior staff I was able to act as his first assistant for minor and major operations such as gastrectomy and resection of bowel. He was a meticulous surgeon who taught me a great deal. His clinical appraisal of patients who were admitted to the ward as emergencies, was particularly impressive. He would take the students to see these patients sometimes several times before he made the decision to operate.

Returning to the Middlesex Hospital in central London, two further three-month periods were completed and these were followed by attachments to specialized firms such as paediatric, midwifery and gynaecology. During midwifery training each student had to deliver twenty babies and this again was carried out at the Central Middlesex hospital. Students were involved in these firms as much as possible in taking case histories and performing investigations and collecting specimens for laboratory analysis.

My "year" consisted of approximately sixty students between half and a third being female. Not all completed the course. I gained considerable support and encouragement from my classmates. Four of us made a habit of taking a packed lunch into the pathological museum. There we quizzed each other on the specimens of diseased organs some of which were available to the examiners in our final qualifying examination. The sharing of knowledge was valuable in helping us to ascertain the depth of factual detail that other students had achieved. Orthopaedic outpatient clinics were important to a potential surgeon as a large portion of the FRCS curriculum is centred on this subject. This includes an understanding of fractures and bony conditions affecting the skeleton. I took a particular interest in this subject. My uncle, Edward Kirk, who had served with Professor John Kirk in the mission field in South China between the two great World Wars suggested that my abilities in woodwork and metal work would be of great value if I became a specialist in this field.

I was leading a "full" life at this time. At one stage I was elected as chairman of the students Common Room. I had to give a vote of thanks to Lord Astor of Heaver, in Kent. He was a most generous supporter of the Middlesex Hospital and Medical School, making many donations to the buildings and equipment. Princess Margaretta of Denmark visited the hospital and with several other students we were given the task of entertaining her and of dancing with her throughout the evening. She was a most charming individual and it was a pleasure to help in entertaining her. During the first year of clinical tuition I was asked to organise the cast for the annual charity concert that was held at the Scala Theatre in

Bloomsbury. I had to persuade the artistes to give their services freely. All proceeds went to cancer research. I visited Tommy Cooper who was admitted to the Italian Hospital in Soho with acute appendicitis. This was a memorable occasion but his jocular laughter was restricted. He was in pain when he laughed but this did not prevent his remarkable personality from coming through. Unfortunately he was not able to take part in what turned out to be a successful venture. "The Three Monarchs" gave us a remarkable exposition of their skilful playing of the harmonica. The concert terminated with a rousing rendition by the Dagenham girls pipe band who marched as they played, kilts swirling, bringing the evening to a rousing conclusion.

The second MB examination is a very stern test of the students' ability to retain an enormous volume of factual knowledge, as well as being a test of stamina and enthusiasm to succeed. One of the objectives of the examiners is to weed out those students who are likely to find it difficult to complete the course, that is, three years of exposure to the wide vista of clinical medicine and surgery. The initial part of the course leads the students into the realm of detective work and the interpretation of "signs and symptoms," which have to be drawn out of the patient's memory. The students are now eligible to purchase their first stethoscope, patella hammer and pocket torch. A stethoscope can come in very handily if the owner has it with him when he is caught exceeding the speed limit by the police.

One of my colleagues, was on call for two hospitals, Broadgreen and Walton. These are situated at either end of a ring-road that forms a circular route around the city of Liverpool. Doctor X had a call from Walton Hospital to Broadgreen, where he was working. He was driving round the ring road to Walton Hospital at a goodly pace. A police car drew alongside doctor X's car and beckoned him to slow down. Doctor X noted his stethoscope on his passenger seat beside him. He picked it up and twirled it out of the driver's window. The police car that was driving in the opposite direction, saluted him and waved him on his way. Having completed his mission at Walton, doctor X was again noticed by the same police car to be exceeding the speed limit as he hurried to get home for a well-earned cup of tea. This time things were a little different as the policeman in the passenger seat was leaning out of the window and was twirling a pair of handcuffs!

There may well be reluctance on the behalf of the patient to divulge their private thoughts and feelings related to their illness. The medical history is probably more important than the physical examination of the patient by the doctor. Taking one's first medical history is a scary experience as the patient probably knows more about their condition than does the student. However, the taking of a detailed medical history is the way the student learns about the relationship between patients and their illnesses. The study of pathology opens a huge branch of medicine to the student. It involves understanding the importance of studying the patient's condition in the laboratory and by non-invasive and invasive "special tests." A vast amount of information can be gained from tests on the patient's blood. Their blood is compared with the normal range within standard deviation, and further special tests may be indicated.

Signs are elicited by visual examination of the patient and by palpation (feeling) with hands and fingers. The student is introduced to the diagnosis of "lumps and bumps." Is the lump solitary or are there others in the same region of the body or at a distance from the original? Another important diagnostic aid is provided by the department of radiology using X-rays. This is of great value in the examination of the chest and heart. Radiology now embraces the science of angiography and of cardiac catheterisation and is closely allied to 3-D echo studies. Other modern developments include specific scanning procedures, such as MRI (magnetic resonance imaging). Gradually, and in pace with the development of modern equipment, for instance the arrival of plastic as a commercial product, great advances have been made in this field. The secret corners of our bodies are now open to inspection by the methods of investigation outlined above. The adage "more mistakes are made by not looking than by not knowing" remains an important truth and is as useful to the student and doctor as it is to a mechanic. Most students find the diverse nature of their medical curriculum fascinating and it is often during the clinical course that a student finds his vocation. In medicine there is something for everyone.

The second and third years of clinical study are taken up with the specialist branches of medicine and surgery. These include anaesthesia, obstetrics and gynaecology, paediatrics and neonatology, cardio-thoracic surgery and tropical medicine.

I include the above outline of medical education to give the lay reader of these memoirs a deeper insight and understanding of the magnitude of the task facing the medical student over his long period of study. The clinician and young student sits, as it were, on a three-legged stool. His ability to be a successful doctor or a weak member of the medical profession depends on the strength of his knowledge represented by the legs of the stool that support him (anatomy, physiology and pathology). During the long course of training it becomes clear to the student where his best ability is centered. Some are destined for academic honours and in teaching. Others have a delicacy of touch that is essential in surgery. Those who prefer their encounters with patients when they are unconscious had better look to anaesthesia or pathology for their livelihood! Academic brilliance is not necessarily an essential ingredient of a student's make-up. I suggest that those of average and just above average ability are suitable candidates for medical training. I put enthusiasm for the job in hand high on my list of priorities for entry to medical school. The actual content of knowledge requires a certain amount of understanding but it is the sheer volume of work in a number of different subjects that demand concentration on the part of the student. Extra curricular activities such as sports, music and outdoor pursuits, for example, beckon the student to give up some of the free time that is available at weekends. Many years later when I was a member of committees choosing candidates for medical and surgical posts I always finished my period of questioning by asking the candidate for some insight into their leisure pursuits. Junior doctors' working hours in hospital are far less demanding today than was the case with my generation. This allows them a better chance to spend time with their families or to practice their chosen hobbies. My own experience supports my belief that it is essential for the medical student to keep up with the course. Discipline is required and I found it necessary to study five nights a week for two to three hours if I were to keep up with the barrage of new material. Once the student has entered the hospital to "walk the wards" he is expected to attend lectures and outpatients clinics. Some students declined to do this and they fell behind as a consequence.

By organising one's timetable it was possible to lead a full life. The captain of Scotland's hockey team and several members of the Middlesex Hospital rugby team were in my year. We also had a female student who played lacrosse for Ireland. The support and encouragement of knowing how fellow students were tackling the task that the course presents was an important factor in maintaining one's effort and drive. As far as the final exam is concerned there are certain rules and procedures that the student would do well to consider. Written essay type questions are less frequently asked than multiple-choice ones. As far as the former are concerned, if you are asked to answer three questions in a three-hour period, give yourself the best chance. Allocate equal time to answering each question. Before writing a definitive answer, make brief notes on all three questions, possibly using some aid memoir. This may be in the form of congenital, inflammatory, traumatic, acute or chronic afflictions. Use such headings to draw the knowledge that has sunk to the depths of your memory to the surface. Excellent textbooks are now available in all subjects. These can be obtained from a medical library and especially helpful texts may be purchased. Choose only books that you feel you will enjoy reading. A book should encourage you to read it. It should be of suitable size with typescript that can be read easily. Books that do not lie open on the table or lap with typescript that is small and that is poorly set out will not be used for study very often.

During the latter part of the student's final year he should have formulated ideas concerning the future. I remember one student who was sitting in the front hall of the Middlesex Hospital having graduated after several attempts. He was as if shell shocked as he had no idea where his future lay. I do not think he had given thought to the possibility that he would one day slip through the examiner's net.

I recommend the concept of a student's house job during the final year of training. I was fortunate to obtain such a job at Kettering General Hospital. I joined Mr Cullen's surgical unit for four weeks as stand in for the appointed houseman who was away on leave. Although I felt very inadequate, I gained confidence through this experience when I took up my post of house surgeon to Mr Vaughan Hudson, senior surgeon at the Middlesex Hospital. I was able to offer at least one personal observation when I was in the sister's office that looked down the full length of the Nightingale ward. The bottom of the ward was occupied by three beds, two of which were angled and the central one looked straight back towards sister's office. I noticed a nurse open the curtains that she had drawn all around the bed a few minutes earlier and was clearly delighted that she had delivered a dose of antibiotic to her unfortunate patient. As she entered the small room where I had been watching, I said to her,

"Mrs Y is not written up for any injections. What have you just given her?"

"Oh indeed, doctor. I knew it was one of them there patients at the bottom of the ward who were meant to have an injection of antibiotic."

Hospitals can be dangerous places!

The academic standard in our year was boosted by the fact that almost half the students were female. In addition, some students joining us for clinical parts of the course were from Oxford and Cambridge. This ensured that the highest standards were maintained. This was borne out by their final appointments to consultant posts years later. The close relationship of students in a particular year became less strong as the course proceeded and each followed their own particular interest in medicine and extra-curricular activities. Gradually, individual talents became evident. Some joined the dramatic society who performed shows of a high standard, and most joined the medical society who had an interesting programme with visiting speakers. Members of the teaching staff of the hospital and invited experts ensured that a high standard of papers was presented. The biggest audience recorded, with all seats sold, was for a talk on contraception by Marie Stopes, where students competed for places on window ledges on a balmy summer's evening. My own contribution was a paper on Frere Jacques, one of our nursery rhyme heroes. A member of one of the Holy Orders, he practised the art of lithotomy. Bladder stones were a common cause of painful micturition and cutters for stone were in demand. The unfortunate subject was sedated with alcohol by mouth and was given leather to bite on. Divested of his lower clothing, he was positioned on his back on a wooden table and his attendants then drew up his knees to open up the perineal region on either side of the rectum. The lithotomist then plunged his knife into the bladder and followed this by inserting a finger into the bladder from which the stone was extracted. No doubt attempts were made to arrest major haemorrhage but he wasted no time in holding up the stone to his audience. " I have produced the stone. God will heal him." He then mounted his horse and rode away from the scene as quickly as possible. This establishes the important fact that doctors do not have the power of healing themselves, but that they act as agents of our Divine Maker. Only He has the power to heal, building on the work of the surgeon and physician to complete the miracle of healing.

1936 Lagonda Rapier.

Our Engagement Photo

With Myra's parents in their garden

Top Left: David with first born Ian

Top Right: "How are these for size?"
                Ian trying on gumboots

Centre: "Like father, like sons"
                Al and Ross get ready for cricket

Bottom Left: Dad with Ian, James and Al.

SURGICAL TRAINING

During the 1950s, to gain full registration as a medical practitioner, it was necessary to complete two appointments of six months each as a resident in an approved hospital. Most newly qualified doctors applied as their first choice to their own teaching hospital for posts in medicine and surgery. Midwifery and gynaecology could count as medicine or surgery according to the candidate's requirement. I opted for surgery and midwifery and gynaecology as my first choices. My commitment after the interviews was to the senior surgeon, Mr Rupert Vaughan Hudson. Following that I worked under Mr F R Roques, Mr Ralph Winterton and Mr Ian Jackson. One of the issues following from these appointments at the Middlesex Hospital was the consultant's attitude to the hours of work they expected from their junior staff. Mr Vaughan Hudson was well known for the demanding regime he imposed upon his juniors. Quite simply, one was on-call and living in hospital for six months. This created considerable stress in our relationship as newly weds at the time but has also had long-term effects on our marriage. We have had to dig deep into our reserves of moral strength and determination to survive. If we have been severely tested and I appreciate that there are many men in a variety of walks of life who have to be away from home for long periods, we have survived to see our fiftieth wedding anniversary in November 2007. The physical demands of the on-call system very nearly broke my spirit and Myra's. In some cases they caused breakdowns in general and in mental health. No time off was given following the nights of "call duty" and there was no half-day during the week or the weekend. During the first six months the team under Vaughan Hudson was on-call every fourth week for emergency cases admitted during the evening and night. The house surgeon had to clerk the patient in, taking a full history and carry out the preliminary medical examination. He would then request appropriate X-Rays and blood tests according to the nature of the patient's condition. He would seek a discussion with the senior registrar or consultant. One of these would probably come into hospital, sometimes by bicycle, and on one memorable occasion, in full riding kit. These duties concerning emergency admissions were over and above routine cases that also had to be clerked, examined and cared for throughout their stay in the ward. The house surgeon was also expected to carry out dressing of wounds and other such duties requested by senior members of the team. At least two half days per week were committed to assisting in the operating theatre and extra cases would be accommodated at the end of these routine operating sessions. Ward rounds were carried out twice weekly by consultants or the senior registrar and could be on a daily basis particularly if patients had to be nursed for a time in the intensive care ward. House physicians were not required as assistants in the operating theatre and this gave them slightly more breathing space. In a teaching hospital, such as the Middlesex, patients had to be selected for demonstration to students or for lecture courses. It fell to the junior staff to prepare for demonstration lectures for the students.

Medical students were split into "firms" of eight and were distributed under the consultants concerned with each speciality.

Working for Mr Vaughan Hudson was nevertheless a great experience and a great privilege. His operative technique was outstanding in its delicacy and care of the tissues on which he was working. He was particularly interested in surgery of the thyroid gland. His interest spread beyond the total and partial removal of this organ. He encouraged Roitt and Deborah Donniach in their work which led to a better understanding of auto-immune diseases but in particular of Hashimoto's Thyroiditis.

Vaughan Hudson was a somewhat intimidating figure. On one occasion, when he was operating with a scrub nurse who had not taken a case with him previously, she inadvertently knocked a small pair of haemostatic forceps off the Mayo table onto the floor. This caused alarm, if not panic, amongst those present at the operation. Because there was a delay in getting the surgery under way again, he moved to the patient's feet and flicked about ten Mayo forceps off the sterile table on to the floor. To her great credit, the scrub nurse remained calm and said to him, "and now we must wait until the forceps have been re-sterilised."

The tension in the theatre was electric but the operation was completed successfully in stony silence.

During this period of residency I got to know a patient called Mr Stevens who lived in Grantham. I assisted with the repair of his inguinal hernia and in return he sent Myra and me a delicious Melton Mowbray pie each Christmas for many years.

He came to the Middlesex hospital from Grantham as many patients believed at that time that surgery performed in the great British cities was better than that performed in the provinces. I had quite a lot to do with his care including helping him to bath as he was a large figure. His literary style was unique and gave me many a chuckle.

I was grateful for the watchful eye of Bill Richardson, who came to the Middlesex, as a Travelling Fellow from Dunedin, New Zealand, in the place of my cousin, Christopher Stubbs who was unable to take up the scholarship that he had won as he had too many children to accompany him. John Fleming was also a good friend to have in the post of registrar.

I do not know for sure, but I imagine that Mr Vaughan Hudson came to forgive me for failing to notice that one of our patients required urinary bladder catheterisation on my first day in office. He wrote to me in short letters several times subsequent to my appointment as his house surgeon. He moved to Wales in retirement but sadly his eyesight deteriorated and I believe failed altogether eventually. He was a great inspiration to me as his junior assistant, not long before his retirement.

And so to gynaecology and midwifery:

In my final viva examination in these subjects, one of my examiners was Sir Arthur Bell, who was a consultant in London's Westminster Hospital. We happened to live near him in Claygate, in Surrey. He had a fine garden that was tended by an elderly gardener who was of discerning character. Vegetables from the garden were sold to the public on the pavement that ran alongside his property. Myra was purchasing some of his produce one day when the gardener appeared and they fell into conversation. Myra told him that his employer had recently examined me in my final qualifying exams. She added that he had a fine reputation in London,

"Yes, Ma'am. He's clever with the ladies, very clever."

The senior gynaecologist at the Middlesex was Mr Freddie R Roques. He was a surgeon of the old school, a larger than life character. He lived outside Cambridge and travelled home in the evening from Liverpool Street station, leaving the patient on whom he was operating in the hands of the senior registrar and house surgeon. The latter had assisted him thus far in his operating list. The senior registrar stood behind the house surgeon before he assumed the role of operative surgeon. Freddie Roques could perform the operation of total hysterectomy in twenty minutes provided he had a dexterous assistant. The surgeon and assistant each had a reel of catgut mounted on a spool on their wrist. Freddie had a small pair of scissors hidden in the palm of one hand. When it was time to ligate the structures forming the round ligament of the uterus, he circumnavigated this anatomical structure with a large circular Reveden's needle. The assistant pulled off the spool a length of catgut from the chief's wrist or from his own. This was then offered up to the consultant in a suitable way for him to cut the catgut with his scissors. This "leger de main" turned operating into something of a theatrical entertainment.

His value as an entertainer came to the fore on another occasion when I was assisting him. The patient's right leg began to move under the sterile drapes. I managed to restrain its activity for some time but the movements increased until everyone in theatre saw the leg elevate to about 45 degrees from the horizontal. His anaesthetist was a senior member of the Faculty of Anaesthetists, nevertheless Freddie went for him as follows,

"Bernard, you've been on holiday. You've forgotten how to do it," he jibed. The anaesthetist hurried to inject another dose of sedative and analgesic into the intravenous drip. Meanwhile the patient's leg movements increased. I then felt a squelching sensation in my left gumboot. We sometimes wore these short white rubber gumboots when operating.

"Excuse me, Mr Roques," I said, "but my left boot is filling up with fluid. So perhaps the drip has become disconnected. My left foot must be being anaesthetised instead of the patient!"

Another task that fell to the house surgeon in midwifery was to carry out vaginal repair by suture at the time of a birth when an episiotomy had been required. The call came at any time of the day or night to go to the labour theatre to carry out this important piece of surgery. The patient was organized into the lithotomy position in the same way that Frere Jacques would have used when cutting for bladder stones. I was called one night in the small hours and went straight to sleep again. The phone eventually went at about six in the morning and I was extremely embarrassed that I had failed in my duty and this lady had suffered the discomfort of being "up in stirrups" for several hours.

Much of gynaecological practice was carried out in outpatient clinics. As students, we had attended some of these clinics at Soho's Hospital for

Women. The gynaecologist specializes in correction of pathological conditions of the womb. This may undergo benign and malignant change and if the pelvic floor musculature becomes weak, usually due to repeated births, the possibility of resulting prolapse of the uterus may result. This can be treated conservatively by the insertion of a ring pessary. This is inserted in the outpatient clinic and may be successful for a period of time. We heard tell of the unfortunate patient who attended the clinic in the afternoon and left to prepare herself for her husband's firm's annual ball at a large West-End hotel. The couple set off in cheerful mood with their minds set on enjoying themselves. Their hopes of this were shattered when during a "quick step" dance the ring pessary was seen to role smoothly across the wide expanse of the dance floor. A surgical approach could have saved this unfortunate lady's embarrassment. As a surgeon one has to learn the importance of performing the right operation at the right time.

At this time at the Middlesex, Sister Diggle ran the maternity wards. She was a formidable character coming from the Preston Region of Lancashire and had served in the Eighth Army's North African campaign in one of the surgical teams during the Second World War. Our first born son, Ian, was delivered soon after I had completed my six months as House surgeon in her unit. I was working at St. Helier Hospital, Carshalton, as Senior House Officer under Mr Aubrey York Mason when Myra was carrying our second son, James. She telephoned me at the hospital during the night to say that she believed she was starting in labour. Being her second child, I decided not to delay, and said I would drive her straight up to the Middlesex for admission to Sister Diggle's unit. I left Myra in her capable hands and returned to my duties at St. Helier Hospital. At approximately 11am I telephoned the maternity unit and was confronted by an irate Sister,

"Your wife's about as much in labour as I am. She's no good to me. Come and take her away!"

I felt as small as a field mouse. I took Myra in the car to the goods yards at Paddington station and drove slowly over the cobbled stones and railway tracks. This is an unorthodox manner of inducing labour but in this case it worked wonderfully well. James Bruce arrived safely and little did we know that he would pass through the Medical School at the Middlesex Hospital some twenty years later.

I planned my approach to passing the Primary and Final parts of the FRCS examination (London) as if it were a military exercise. Where I wonder did the determination and audacity in doing so come from? There was a dynamo churning away inside me, fuelled by the achievement of several uncles, cousins and friends not to speak of my father's standing in the field of civil engineering. My prayers were aimed at enquiring of God how I should develop the talents that He had given me. I prayed He would give me the mental faculties and practical skills to enable me to pursue such a challenging course. I next required training in casualty, trauma and orthopaedic surgery. I took the advice of Mr Michael Ashken, a member of the winning hospital cricket team who had profited under the guidance of Mr GN Golden, consultant orthopaedic surgeon at the Royal Surrey County Hospital, Guildford.

Being experienced in mechanical matters, I fell quickly into the role of orthopaedic surgeon and was given good experience of pinning fractures of the femoral neck and I began to harbour thoughts of taking bone setting up as a career. However, healing of fractures is a slow process and the appeal of handling the softer tissues of the body lured me towards general surgery.

My first experience of handling patients who had sustained multiple skeletal injuries came at 5am one morning with an urgent telephone call to attend the casualty department immediately. Five or six teenagers had driven up the motorway to a party in London the evening before. On the return journey, in the small hours of the night, the driver was stopped and cautioned by police for speeding. A few miles further on the car plunged off the road and came to rest having struck a large tree. Two of the occupants were pronounced dead on arrival at the casualty department. One was relatively well and survived, one was fortunate to survive without major surgery, although requiring treatment for fractures. Two sixteen year old girls were in severe shock, pulses barely palpable, heart sounds scarcely audible and their faces as white as the wall. Clearly they were desperately short of circulating blood volume and needed massive transfusion as quickly as possible. Two of us would-be-surgeons, took each of these girls in hand as we "cut down" on the long Saphenous veins. The Saphenous vein (meaning easily seen) passes down the inside of the ankle in a position that is constant in relation to surrounding structures. It is easily isolated for the insertion of a cannula that can carry large volumes of blood and fluid and gravity feed can be enhanced with various types of pump. Six pints of blood were pumped into the young girls circulation before their colour returned with pink hue and their heart-beat strengthened as they readily accepted blood donation and plasma expansion. These two young girls suffered terrible injuries. These included fractures of the pelvis, tibia, fibula and femur, and ruptured spleen. Both spent months on the ward on traction and lived to recount their sorry story to their many relations and friends. Youth is loathe to listen to experience and has to learn for herself of the stark realities of life that in time embrace us all.

This experience gave me great confidence in the power of the young to recover from very serious injury. The mechanism to repair and heal that our Creator has organized within the human body is miraculous.

Much of my relationship with Mr Golden took place on the telephone. I learned to give him accurate and detailed descriptions of fractures taken from the clinical findings and X-Ray appearances of the new casualties arriving in the department. My chief gave me considerable operating experience. This was exemplified by the case of a young motorcycle enthusiast who spent months in the ward with a fractured femur. His treatment included the insertion of a so-called "nail" that extended through the full length of the bone from hip to knee. This method of internal fixation should allow early mobilization of the patient and result in a shorter stay in hospital. This patient was eventually discharged only to be re-admitted some few weeks later, having smashed his motorcycle and himself as severely as in the first accident. The Kunsher nail had not escaped the trauma and was angled at its midpoint some twenty five to thirty degrees out of line. I was delegated the task of removing the angulated metal object and replacing it with a straight one. Extraction of a straight nail should not pose any great problems to the surgeon but when angulated the nail will not withdraw easily and in this case it proved extremely difficult to shift. Eventually we succeeded in our task, Mr Golden having joined the team and the operation was completed successfully.

I now had to complete a four year period of surgical training that included casualty (A&E) and orthopaedic surgical experience. I was appointed SHO (Senior House Officer) under Mr Aubrey York Mason who was an examiner for the final FRCS exams at the Royal College of Surgeons in London. He was consultant in General Surgery at St Helier Hospital, in Carshalton, Surrey. This was a busy post, two trainee senior house officers were responsible for seventy beds. The senior and middle grade registrars were both Australian at the time I was attached to the unit. Mark Shanahan, who later became a cardiac surgeon in Sydney, and Paul Steadman filled the middle grade posts. Both were keen to obtain as much operative experience as they could. Never the less I was delegated cases of acute appendicitis and several cholecystectomies (removal of gall bladder) and other operations within my capabilities. Aubrey York Mason was a keen tennis player, coming from South Africa. He had a grass tennis court in his garden and was an enthusiastic participator in the game, as was Paul Steadman. Myra and I were very pleased to be asked to join one of his tennis parties. Ian, our first-born son, knocked over a glass of South African sherry onto his lawn. This did not go down at all well, Mr York Mason exclaiming,

"My best South African sherry!"

I think we surprised the company with our ability to play to a good standard as we had not played since the Army tennis championship in which I represented the Royal Signals in 1951, some ten years previously.

Following this appointment I took time out and attended a course at St Thomas' hospital in London that was designed specifically for candidates for the final FRCS exam in clinical surgery. I had obtained the primary FRCS exam in Glasgow at the end of my period of fifteen months as demonstrator and lecturer in Professor Eldred Walls department at the Middlesex Hospital. Eldred Walls was from Glasgow. He succeeded my uncle, John Kirk, in the Chair and he was an inspiring personality and teacher. I studied extremely hard at anatomy, revising on the journey from Claygate in Surrey to Waterloo station and on the Northern Line of the London Underground. My philosophy was that if I learned anatomy well enough to teach the best medical students I would have achieved my preparation of this subject adequately. My teaching was appreciated and I developed a happy relationship with the students, nurses and physiotherapists. A week before I travelled to Glasgow for the primary fellowship exam I asked the professor if he would be kind enough to give three of us a mock examination consisting of questions using a cadaver in the dissecting room. I can only think that the professor was taking this opportunity to keep me in my place as I had expressed an interest in taking up anatomy teaching as a career. His advice was that I should get back into clinical training as quickly as possible as he considered that surgery was where my calling lay. I believe I was able to answer only one of the questions he put to me and again I felt like the "timorous mousie" of Robert

Burns.

The course at St Thomas' Hospital for candidates sitting the final FRCS exam was most valuable particularly in two aspects. One was the students' depth of knowledge revealed by the teachers' questioning. Secondly, we had to sit under examination conditions and had to answer past examination questions on a weekly basis.

The final exam for Fellowship of The Royal College of Surgeons was in two parts, written and oral. The written paper was in the form of essay writing being before the changeover to multiple choice questions. The first questions were straight forward but there was one backhander that could not have been expected.

"Discuss the causes of ischaemia of the abdominal viscera."

Before committing myself to paper I made a list of the large number of anatomical structures that were involved and another list of the various pathological conditions that could cause ischaemia. In this way I brought the knowledge that I had on this topic into relief and this gave my answer some structure. The greater ordeal was the day-long series of viva voce exams. This included the examination of short cases identifying lumps and bumps on patients who had consented to act as models. The examination included a longer case where one had to expound on the clinical findings and treatment of the patient. The pathological viva consisted of identifying preserved specimens from the Pathological Museum but the viva that stands out in my memory, and always will, was the operative surgery inquisition. I was faced by two examiners and was asked to outline the steps I would take in removing a large malignant tumour from the left kidney. Fortunately, I had attended such an operation only the week before and I was therefore quite certain of my ground. These tumours tend to spread by infiltrating into the renal vein of the kidney. This can result in the dissemination of pieces of the tumour if the kidney is handled without great delicacy. One approach, and the one I chose to describe, entails exposing the kidney and surrounding area by making a thoraco-abdominal incision that opens both chest and abdomen. The diaphragm has to be divided diametrically. This is a formidable procedure but enables the surgeon to have superb access and enables him to remove the whole kidney and any tumour without any danger of spread of malignant cells. The viva suddenly became a nightmare as one of the examiners took on a somewhat sarcastic tone,

"You don't mean to say that you would open the chest to get to the kidney, do you?"

I decided in a brief moment to stand my ground,

"Yes, I do, and I have given my reasons for making such a long incision."

The examiner persisted in querying my replies to his questions but I was able to justify my apparent audacity. In these moments I was certain that I had blown all hope of passing the exam.

It seemed to me that I might have missed the opportunity of my life, as I sensed that I had passed the other parts of the examination all of which had gone smoothly.

You can imagine the euphoria that flooded through my veins when I saw my name was included with the relatively few others who passed on that occasion.

I was now in a position to apply for a new post of rotating surgical registrar at the Middlesex Hospital. My success was noted by Sir Eric Riches who was a regular supporter of the hospital rugby team. He stopped me in the main corridor and made the comment,

" I thought you might just sneak through!"

Thus ended my quest to become a member of the Royal College of Surgeons of England. Thus my third ambition was achieved.

And so at the age of thirty my three boyhood ambitions were finally accomplished and the "improbable" had become a reality. A further period of training of six years awaited me before I was appointed as the first full-time cardiac surgeon in Liverpool.

The swings and roundabouts of these events are hard to accept unless you acknowledge the power of The Almighty and know that He is at the Helm, making all things possible.

Sir Thomas Holmes Sellors,
P.R.S.C.S.Eng.

Professor P.F. Jones, F.R.C.S.

Sir J. Keith Ross, M.S., F.R.C.S.

Mother Janet with baby Dawn

Baby Dawn who had major cardiac reconstruction. Wedding bells 20 years later!

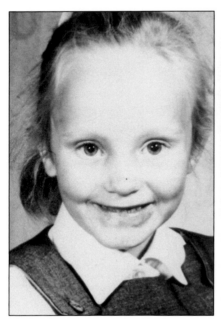

Before and after "Blue Baby Surgery".

DECISIONS, DECISIONS!

The first six months as rotating surgical registrar at the Middlesex Hospital commenced on the 1st of January 1962. I began working under Sir Thomas Holmes Sellors and Mr J Belcher who were the two senior surgeons in the department of cardiothoracic surgery. Sir Thomas and Sir Russell Brock were two of the early pioneers of chest surgery before, during and after the Second World War. My sister, Anne, and I used to enjoy Christmas parties with Russell Brock's daughters as we lived near each other in Wimbledon. Another surgeon who had a strong influence on my development as an operative surgeon was Keith Ross, later Sir Keith Ross. We played together winning through five preliminary rounds of the Middlesex seven a side rugby football competition. The following Saturday we ran out onto Twickenham's famous pitch, full of hope and expectation. We were very quickly brought down to earth by the team representing St Thomas' hospital. As a heart and lung team we were more successful in the operating theatre than on the rugby pitch. This was just as well for our patients. However, the training in teamwork and cooperation that team games provided paved the way for success professionally. At this time I had no intention of a career in cardiac surgery. The working of the heart lung machine was of particular interest and I did some early research work in this field.

The second six month period saw me as registrar to Sir Eric Riches and Mr O Lloyd Davies. I also worked under Mr Richard T Turner Warwick, a very talented surgeon in the field of Urological conditions. The final stage of training as a registrar was completed as assistant to Mr David Patey and Mr Leslie LeQuesne. I had some exposure to research technique during this time and my operative skills were tested. Mr Ian Ranger, the senior registrar, was on extended leave following an attack of infective Hepititis at this time. I was able to "act up" and was given every opportunity by my superiors. But the future still remained shrouded in uncertainty.

I was walking down the main corridor of the hospital one day, and was rapidly approached by Sir Thomas Holmes Sellors. He stopped, "What are you doing?"

"I am looking for a senior registrar post. Jobs are not easy to come by at the moment."

"Just the man I want," he replied. "I've recently returned from examining in the Sudan, and they want someone to go out there and teach them cardiothoracic surgery!"

The broad implications of this statement stunned me.

"Go and talk with that wife of yours and come back in the morning with your decision."

Myra had worked for some time as a physiotherapist on his wards and she had also treated him for a frozen shoulder when her senior colleague was indisposed.

We had always considered working abroad as surgeon missionaries to be one of our options. We met in the morning and I told him that we were prepared to go to the Sudan provided that I could obtain training in the management of Tuberculosis. His repost to that suggestion was,

"Come to Harefield and we'll give you a crash course in Tubercle!"

Uncle Tom (as he was known affectionately) was a fine artist and he spoke in sweeping terms, making the unlikely possible.

Two things followed from this conversation. Yes, I did go to Harefield as a registrar but did not see a single case of TB and no we did not go to the Sudan for reasons outwith our control. Nevertheless, these conversations with Uncle Tom changed the direction of my career. The registrar appointment at Harefield was very busy. My fellow surgical registrar was Miss Mary Shepherd, a powerful colleague who later distinguished herself as one of Professor Bob Anderson's team, based at the Brompton Hospital. He presented cardiac anatomy and morphology to the world. This might not have happened had I not placed a suture around the conduction bundle during the closure of a Ventricular septal defect. This stimulated Bob Anderson to investigate the anatomy of one of the heart's vital structures in greater detail. And so started a life's work in exposing the detailed anatomy of the specialized conducting tissue in all types of congenital cardiac defects.

My tenure of the post at Harefield depended on my having transport that would convey me reliably between Claygate, in Surrey, and Harefield,

North West of London. As Myra required our car for making school runs, I had to use the 1936 Austin Seven that I had completely rebuilt. This splendid vehicle, though small of stature, proved to be extremely reliable and seldom let me down. I used to leave home soon after 6am and drove into the hospital grounds within the hour. Although I was shocked by the high proportion of patients with malignant conditions, it was during this appointment that I decided to spend my future career in Cardiothoracic surgery. In this decision I was influenced by the dedication and skill of Sir Thomas Holmes Sellors, John Jackson and Sir Keith Ross, in particular.

The appointment to work as cardiac surgeon in Kartoum went to a much more senior surgeon than me and I took up the post of registrar under Sir Thomas at Harefield. The time passed very quickly and I now required training at senior registrar level and became interested in an advertisement that offered experience in both paediatric and adult cardiothorasic surgery in Liverpool. It was unlikely that I could obtain such a wide spectrum of training in a single appointment had I stayed in London. Myra's aunt lived in her family's holiday home in Wigtown in South West Scotland. Staying with her during the war years was a family by the name of Bickford who had remained in touch with her, spending holidays in that region of Scotland. John Bickford had been medical officer and surgeon to the RAF training station at Baldoon. After the war he became one of six chest surgeons working in Liverpool. I had several telephone conversations with him and after much deliberation, decided to apply for this post. Ronald Edwards and Leslie Temple had pioneered paediatric and adult open heart surgery and had built up very successful teams and had large waiting lists of patients. Sir Thomas Holmes Sellors took me into the board room at Harefield one morning and we sat at one end of the lengthy table,

"What's this I hear about you applying to Liverpool?" and he inferred that he was not in favour of this move.

I replied that I was confident that the team in Liverpool had already achieved much and was capable of further development in the future. During the next few days I was persuaded to withdraw my application to Liverpool but I came to feel unhappy about this. Life was miserable as I felt I was going against God's guidance in this matter. I telephoned John Bickford and apologized for withdrawing from the appointments committee at which no-one was appointed. My internal struggle raged fiercely during the next few weeks. Finally, I gave way to my feelings and picked up the telephone again,

"If I promise not to withdraw a second time will you reconvene the appointments committee?"

I was duly appointed towards the end of 1964.

This was the year that my mother died, weakened and finally overcome by ovarian malignancy. She was sadly not able to be present at the opening of the Forth Road Bridge in Edinburgh. This was my father's final duty as Resident Engineer, apart from some responsibilities in an advisory capacity in the final phases in the construction of the bridge over the River Severn, near Bristol. He enjoyed his retirement years and if my mother's death was drawn out over a period of one year, my father passed away very suddenly. I was holidaying with the family on our canal boat in Worcestershire when I spied a young policeman walking along the tow path towards us. I knew instinctively he was bringing bad news to us. After establishing our identity, he said your father is very ill in Edinburgh,

"Is he still alive?" I asked.

"No, Sir, he passed away earlier this morning."

He had gone to the shops for food for a small dinner party with some friends. The list of items he had chosen, that was found in his coat pocket included avocado pears! Whilst waiting in a short queue he fell backwards, hitting his head on a rack of bottles. Folk went to his assistance but he sat up and said,

"I shall be alright now."

As they went to his aid he fell back a second time and passed away. It was the way he would have chosen himself. He disliked hospitals and medical matters, possibly as a result of his horrific experiences as a seventeen year old ambulance driver in the First World War. I wish to pay tribute to my parents who were both outstanding characters being true to their faith and stalwarts in the tasks to which they had set their hands. They did not spare themselves in giving Anne and me opportunities in life that I trust we have developed in a way that would please them.

The family now faced the formidable task of packing up our home in Claygate and leaving the London area that had been our stamping ground for nearly thirty years. With the help of Geoffrey Sykes, a leading estate agent and distant cousin of my father's, we found a suitable home in Hightown, North of Liverpool. This necessitated a drive of thirty to forty minutes to the adult regional cardiothoracic unit at Broadgreen hospital in Liverpool.

The journey North was accomplished in two cars. We broke the trip some thirty five miles South of Liverpool for tea.

"Where was Morag?" I asked, she being our resident border terrier at that time.

In Claygate she had survived an accident resulting in a fractured pelvis. We had decided to nurse her in a corner of the dining room in a bed specially constructed for her needs. In reply to my question, I was told that I should have had her in my car. It soon became clear that she was missing. I had seen her last at a petrol filling station at Watford Gap on the M1. We completed our journey to Hightown, disembarked and I retraced my steps to Watford Gap. There was no sign of this splendid little creature who was such an important member of our family. However, after one week we had a telephone call from the Surrey police telling us that she had been found on a farm and we were invited to go and collect her. In due course the whole family was thrilled to be reunited once more.

The move to Liverpool was clearly a major event in our family's life. We were fortunate to find a suitable house in Elmcroft Lane that had been built by a timber merchant. The garden was of average dimensions and the railway from Liverpool to Southport ran past it. It caused Myra and me some concern for the children's safety. In fact our concerns were ill-founded and we need not have feared.

The consultants who worked in the cardiothoracic surgical unit at Broadgreen and the Royal Liverpool Children's Hospital had a different attitude towards their junior staff than was customary in London. They viewed the senior registrar's position as similar in seniority to the registrars in the unit with the additional responsibility of organising the "on-call" rota. I managed to persuade them to take the senior registrar out of the rota by making him available to the consultants should they require more senior assistance. The senior registrar remained attached to each of the consultants in rotation. There was no established post for cardiothoracic surgery at The Royal Liverpool Children's Hospital. The first assistant for the operations on children was filled by one of the registrars who was working at Broadgreen Hospital chest unit. One spin-off from this system was that the children in the cardiac intensive care ward were supervised to a large extent by the cardiologists and paediatric anaesthetists. The surgeons paid supervisory visits, usually twice daily and made themselves available. As Sir Thomas Holmes Sellors had predicted, I found the management and performance of surgery to be somewhat different as that practised in London. I was attached to each of the consultants in Liverpool in rotation and gained from their wide experience. The unit at Broadgreen served a catchment area that included the North West region of England. This extended to North of Cumberland and as far South as Birmingham. To the West, the coastline including the Isle of Man and to the East, it abutted on the Manchester region. Outlying clinics had been built up with the expansion of thoracic surgery and these included the Isle of Man, North Wales, The Wirral and Warrington. Major surgery, such as lung resection was performed in some of these outlying units.

Before leaving the Middlesex Hospital, I had discussed the possibility of working under Dr Frank Gerbode at the Presbyterian Medical Centre in San Francisco. Sir Keith Ross introduced me to him and he accepted my application for a travelling fellowship of one year's duration. Frank Gerbode was one of America's pioneering heart surgeons who perfected a membrane oxygenator with the help of Dr Osborne and the engineering skills of Mr Bramson. During the war Bramson had developed a timing mechanism for aeroplanes that carried guns mounted in their wings. This enabled them to keep firing as the bullets were timed to avoid damaging the propeller blades. His membrane heart lung machine was extremely efficient but required considerable volumes of blood used in priming and in oxygenation. I had mentioned that I wished to be released from my duties to take up this Fellowship to the appointments committee at Liverpool. Ronald Edwards expressed his concern at my leaving Broadgreen even temporarily, so soon after I had arrived. He spoke to me one afternoon, saying,

"Do you really think that going to America will make you a better surgeon?"

"I am sure that it will," was my reply.

As I was determined to take the whole family now consisting of Myra, and sons, Ian, James, Alastair and Ross, I was finding it hard to raise sufficient funding. But help was at hand. The Liverpool regional health authority made a substantial contribution. Within a few weeks of our date of departure, an advertisement appeared in the British Medical Journal advertising the Comyns-Berkeley travelling fellowship (in association with Caius College, Cambridge). I was interviewed for this scholarship at the Middlesex Hospital and had just been called before the committee when the door of the room I was to be interviewed in opened and the familiar figure of Mr Leslie LeQuesne joined the appointments panel. He had been my chief in general surgery in the department of surgical studies at the Middlesex Hospital. He must have put some considerable support behind me as I was fortunate to be elected as Comyns-Berkeley fellow during our year in the USA.

The family's departure from Liverpool in September 1966, when we sailed in the SS Corinthia, was the last passenger voyage before the service closed down. We very nearly missed the boat for this five day voyage to Montreal. In fact we probably would have done so, had it not been for the stalwart assistance of the Bickford sons, Rawley and Oliver. The Corinthia was just about to slip her moorings when we arrived with the car heavily laden and the Bickford's car also weighed down by the quantity of luggage we considered essential for our trip. We were not popular!

Our fourth son, Ross, had been born in our house at Hightown in July 1965. His lifespan might have been cut tragically short had it not been for an alert father who seized him with both hands as he crawled rapidly towards the rail when we were resting on deck on our voyage. Soon after our arrival in America we flew to San Francisco where we had booked an apartment for one week. There followed a hectic search for suitable accommodation within easy reach of the hospital. Within a few days we had found a suitable dwelling in the Sunset area of the city. A second hand Chevy Estate was purchased and later a VW Beetle was acquired for Myra's school runs. These automobiles brought their adventures with them. I was on call duty in the intensive care ward one night. I went to the car park early next morning to find that the car was missing. I got a phone call about a week later to say that it was in a police compound in the northern region of the city. I found my way to the police station in question and will never forget the atmosphere of that place. Police staff were everywhere. Big strong macho policemen sitting at desks with guns strapped to their chests chewing gum and some smoking. They said the car had been used by youths in a race and subsequently abandoned. Nevertheless this car served us well and completed many trips out of the city to places of interest.

Our Travelling Fellowship to San Francisco coincided with the Hippy Movement that was in full swing at this time. The city was full of visitors from all corners of the globe. It was cosmopolitan and music filled the air. Clothing was colourful and was readily available at every street corner. We had little time to become involved with the many activities that this movement embraced but the flamboyant lifestyle was evident everywhere. We soon appreciated that people worked hard during the five week days and many left the city during Friday afternoon to pursue their favourite recreations that were an important part of their lifestyle. Many sought open air pursuits according to the season. We purchased a pop tent and went camping in preparation for our six week trip homeward at the end of our year's visit where we camped and motored our way following the route of Trans Canada One. The Chevrolet estate car trunk door opened upwards and the pop tent flap fitted over this making a wide opening between the two. One memorable visit was to a Rodeo at Salinas River, near Sacramento. We sat high up in one of the stands and watched the wide variety of events. The sun beat down upon us and music and announcements interrupted a hectic schedule of bronco-bucking, calf-lassoing, marionette marching and waffle-munching. Another unforgettable winter weekend was spent as the guests of Dr Frank Gerbode in his chalet at the ski resort at the Sugar Bowl in the hills outside San Francisco. During the previous weeks, Myra had managed to obtain suitable clothing for the six members of the family. Without this the boys would have succumbed to the freezing temperatures of the resort's winter conditions. In spite of our efforts to supply suitable protection against the low temperatures, the youngest boys suffered as they were not able to ski.

My duties as a Travelling Fellow kept me well occupied as a member of the clinical team in the Presbyterian Medical Centre. Also in the operating theatre, research laboratory and library. Each visiting Fellow was committed to carrying out a program of research that had to be completed by the time he was due to return to his home base. My chosen research topic was accepted by Dr Gerbode as it fitted in with work completed by a previous Fellow from Australia. This was on the subject of: "Replacement of the Pathological Mitral Valve." At the time I left Liverpool for the USA, we were gaining experience of replacing the human aortic valve with a homograft substitute. Success was achieved in this field by Sir Brian Barratt Boyes of Auckland, New Zealand and by Donald Ross in London. The advantage of using tissue valves in humans compared with the trusted mechanical prosthetic valve was that the former did not require the patients to take anticoagulation therapy for the rest of their lives. At this time, in the 1960's, there was no tissue valve that was suitable as a mitral valve replacement. I was pleased when I heard from Dr Gerbode that he could provide the necessary facilities in his surgical laboratory for replacing the mitral valve in dogs with pig aortic valves. These experiments were necessary from two points of view in particular. Firstly, to study the fate of a tissue heart valve in another species (heterograft), and secondly, whether it was possible to adapt an aortic valve for long term replacement of the complex mitral valve. This surgical technique is described in more detail elsewhere in this book.

Overseas Fellows were expected to assist members of the home team in the operating theatre several times each week and were often invited to discuss differences in approach and operative techniques. Different ideas were debated freely.

The third aspect of my work in America involved nights on call in the intensive care ward. This came round quite frequently as Fellows were encouraged to visit other cardiac units for a week or more. This diminished the number of staff available to cover the ward duties.

Soon after our arrival in San Francisco I was included in the rota as surgeon on duty in the ITU one night. Dr Gerbode had operated on a young girl of about ten years of age. I made a round of the ward at approximately 7pm and assessed the progress of the patients who had undergone open heart surgery earlier that day. This young girl had closure of a large hole in the heart (atrial septal defect). She was in excellent condition with normal pulse rate. She was of good colour, conscious and stable blood pressure. One hour later I visited this girl again and noted dramatic changes in her physical signs. She looked pale, restless with a rapid heart and pulse rate, her pulse being of low volume and most dramatically, her urine output had virtually ceased. I decided without delay that she had internal bleeding around the heart and cardiac compression (tamponade). This is a potentially lethal situation as it can result in inadequate cardiac output. I decided to reopen her surgical incision that would relieve the pressure on her heart and to ascertain the source of hemorrhage. This caused some consternation amongst the nursing staff who no doubt wondered what this newly arrived Fellow from Liverpool thought he was doing. The necessary surgical instruments were nevertheless provided quickly and by the time one of Dr Gerbode's permanent assistants arrived the girl's cardiac compression had been relieved and her blood pressure and heart rate had returned towards normal.

Dr Gerbode had approximately six Fellows from the United States and Europe working in his department at any one time. I spent much of this in his laboratory experimenting with the concept of using an aortic valve with its surrounding aortic wall placed upside down in the mitral ring of the recipient. Other workers had shown that transplanting a healthy mitral valve into a heart was not successful. This was largely due to the fact that the sub leaflet chordae failed to remain attached to the receipient papillary muscles. There is a major difference in the anatomy of the two valves. The aortic valve as prepared in my experiments consisted of a cylinder within which the three aortic leaflets are situated. The mitral valve is mounted on a ring within the floor of the left atrium. The leaflets are then tensioned through the cordae and papillary muscles. I had to make several modifications to the initial experimental model before success was achieved. The longest surviving dog that had received a pig aortic valve in this way was extremely fit initially and survived three months before succumbing to cardiac failure. Whereas I was slightly disappointed in this failure of longer term survival, Dr Gerbode was pleased with the results of my work and supported the concept of heterograft replacement of heart valves in humans.

This project took me on a trip to Chicago. I visited Dow Corning where many types of Sialastic materials were produced. I was looking for a man-made material that might be used to replace damaged valve leaflets. I also visited the team that was led by Dr Albert Starr in Portland, Oregon. He was one of the pioneers in using a Sialastic or hollow metal ball in his prosthetic heart valve. During my visit I attended an operation carried out by Dr Starr and I remember feeling chilled. I ascertained that the regular members of his team were wearing two surgical gowns. This was because he was using a degree of hypothermia achieved by cooling the circulating blood in the heart lung machine. This brought added safety to the patient. When the valve was required to close, the higher pressure in the heart forced the ball onto its seating. When open, the valve flew off its seating and was captured by the cage as the blood flowed through and as the ventricle filled with blood again. This cycle was repeated over and over again. We took one of the surviving dogs on a trolley covered over with a blanket from the animal department and used the public lift to the X-Ray department in the basement of the hospital. The look on the visitor's faces when the dog's tail dropped down below the blanket into view will never be forgotten. The dog was catheterized passing a fine tube from its groin vein back towards the heart. When sited securely in the right ventricle, a mechanical pump delivered a bolus of radio opaque contrast medium into and through the lung circulation and into the left ventricle and beyond. This demonstrated that the aortic valve was functioning perfectly in its new mitral position. The consultant radiologist warmed to his task as he saw the perfect function of my graft in the dog's heart.

"Holy mackerel," he exclaimed, "that valve functions better than anything I've seen in human patients. Why can't we learn to do that!"

The cusps were outlined and were fully competent with no leak and the valve ring was of adequate diameter.

This work I reported to the Society of Cardiothoracic Surgeons of Great Britain and Ireland at their annual meeting held at Southampton in the autumn of 1968. Sir Magdi Yacoub attended this meeting and used this technique in many of his patients subsequently.

We have enduring memories of our year in this amazing city where every nationality is represented and life is colourful. My senior consultant, Ronald Edwards, visited the Presbyterian Medical Centre and attended the annual meeting of the American Association of Cardiothoracic Surgeons. He also came to see one of my operations in progress in the laboratory and spent some time with Dr Gerbode. Ronald Edwards took Myra and me to one of the splendid fish restaurants at Fisherman's Wharf. He was surprised by my choice of lunch that day:

"Have what you like," he said.

Taking him at his word, I asked for lobster thermidor! He may have paled a little but he took it on the chin and it remains one of the highlights of my gastronomic experience!

I was asked to sit on a panel selected from the parents of our older boys' school for a question and answer evening. We were asked to introduce ourselves outlining what we were doing. Not wanting to divulge that my occupation was somewhat unusual, I stated that I was a carpenter, only of soft tissues. I believe this did not go down too well with the audience as they thought I was pulling their legs.

Myra was driving in her VW Beetle near the boy's school when she passed a man who resented her overtaking him, and immediately started to follow her. As she approached traffic lights, they turned red and she was forced to stop. The pursuing driver got out of his car and put his hand on Myra's car door. Fortunately the light turned green and she was able to give him the slip as he was caught with another red light further down the road. She was so shaken by this experience that she had to send her babysitter, who was minding Ross, home by taxi.

The priority between home and hospital life is one of the many difficulties that faces a surgeon day by day. The standard teaching of "knife before wife" comes to mind in this context again. I was in the laboratory one afternoon when I was called to the telephone and Myra's voice came over the line from Yosemite National Park, some two hundred and fifty miles away. She stated,

"We're here in Yosemite. If you want us you'll have to come and get us!" On this occasion I knew where my priority lay and I arrived to join her and the boys before sundown. It is still a joy to this day to have a wife who speaks her mind! This weekend proved to be one of the year's highlights because we were together as a family which was a rare occurrence for us in America. This exemplifies the pressure a surgeon's wife is put under.

This was a momentous year and was of fundamental importance to my development as a cardiac surgeon. I learned the anatomical details of the conducting mechanism and the propagation of the heart beat through that organ by following Dr Gerbode's magnificent slide collection. This stimulated me to start my own collection that came to well over two thousand photographic slides and artists drawings.

This was probably the second phase of my development as a surgeon of congenital heart disease. There are at least a hundred variations in the anatomy of the heart. These are congenital defects (holes in the heart, abnormalities in the formation of the valves and more complex conditions). The greater the knowledge of the surgeon who performs such operations, the quicker he is able to recognize exactly what he has to do.

We had reserved a period of six weeks at the end of the summer planning to camp through Oregon to visit my first cousin, Elisabeth, (nee Kirk) and her husband, Dr Michael Cooper, in Victoria Island, British Columbia. In preparation for our journey across Canada, using Trans Canada Freeway, we had not appreciated that the Chevy Estate car was about to pack up.

This in fact happened on only the second day out of San Francisco. We left the boys in a motel room and Myra and I walked "the car lots" throughout the night searching for a replacement vehicle. Eventually we found a large Dodge station wagon and telephoned my father in England asking him to back us up through the bank to enable us to purchase this replacement car.

Everything was arranged by mid morning on the following day. The car ran perfectly until we approached Montreal. Here she developed a classical motor boat like noise that appeared to come from under the floor of the vehicle. I crawled beneath the car with difficulty and found no such pathology. We motored on to the next large garage and they could find nothing wrong with the exhaust system. We called at two more filling stations but they could find no fault. Eventually on the outskirts of the city we stopped at a service station and told them our tale.

"Wait by your car and I will send an engineer to advise you," I was told.

I was disappointed to see a youthful mechanic wearing overalls approaching us some few minutes later. He appeared to me to be not more than eighteen years of age and I was getting short of patience. He got under the car and came out quickly,

"you're quite right, Sir, you have got a hole in your exhaust pipe but you can't see it. You see there are two exhaust pipes in your system, one inside the other."

I was delighted with this young mechanic who clearly understood the workings of my exhaust in detail. We were soon on our way again, the car purring along on terra firma, rather than "chugging up the river in nautical style."

I now faced the challenge of selling the Dodge with her new exhaust system and hoped to make good the short term loan that my father had negotiated for us at the bank. I hawked the car round all sorts of likely buyers in Montreal and was getting nowhere with my salesmanship. I passed a huge saw mill and asked to see the managing director. Rather than showing me any hostility he seemed to be amused by my tale of woe and he bought the vehicle for an acceptable price. We were now free to make our final leg of this epic journey by plane from Montreal to Heathrow, London.

LIFE IN LIVERPOOL

During our year's visit to America we had let out our house in Hightown, near Formby. We repossessed this property briefly before we moved to a three storey semi-detached house in Bertram Drive, Meols, Wirral. This move came about as we decided to send our sons to Kingsmead School, a Christian establishment situated in the same road. This house proved to be an ideal base for the whole family over the next twenty years. The third storey was divided into three small rooms two of which we turned into a large play room. This space was put to good use in the ensuing years. In particular snooker and table-tennis were enjoyed there. I and the two older boys, Ian and James, made a double kayak canoe from a kit of parts which on completion we found to our dismay, was too long to negotiate down the steep stairs. Fortunately, it was possible to lower the canoe to the ground on ropes passed through one of the windows. It seemed as if the canoe was "accident prone." We had arranged to take it to the Dordoigne district of France for our annual summer holiday and had made a strong roof-rack on which she was transported. The canoe was considerably longer than the Volvo estate car that carried the whole family. We encountered heavy traffic congestion on the outskirts of Liverpool on our way South for the crossing of the Channel on our way to France. We made slow progress through Everton, coming to a complete stop at a crossroads. I could see that the car waiting to cross the lights in front of me would be able to pass on its way if I made room for it by backing up. In carrying out this manoeuvre the stern end of the canoe shattered the windscreen of a double-decker bus that had pulled up close behind our car. Fortunately the driver was not impaled and was able to leave his post uninjured but severely shaken. This was an expensive start to the holiday, costing me the price of a replacement windscreen. The strong fibreglass joins and the monofilament nylon suturing stood up to this traumatic experience surprisingly well! The remainder of our trip to the Dordoigne was memorable by virtue of torrential thunderstorms every night throughout the first week of our holiday. We were allowed to strike camp and to sleep in the comparative comfort of the hay loft of one of the farm buildings of the property we were visiting.

During the week leading up to Christmas Myra used to adapt a play such as "Jack and the Beanstalk" or "A Christmas Carol" and produced a script that the boys quickly learned by heart. These provided thespian interludes that became popular with the hospital staff and friends who were invited to attend annually. The audience was accommodated on the landing and the narrow stairway up to the playroom gave an excellent view of the small stage that was fitted with proper curtains. One of the more ingenious props was a beanstalk that grew taller during the performance of this pantomime. One or two friends were called in to augment the cast as was necessary. On one such occasion we invited our butcher who was asked to carve an enormous roast of beef that he had provided.

The garden was well used as a sports field. A goal was erected with netting in an attempt to protect the newly growing vegetables. The garden became a cricket field in the summer. All manner of family activities were carried out and were enjoyed by Phoebe and Harp, the resident Labrador and marmalade cat that were very much part of our family at that time. Harp was an active fisherman and from time to time appeared on the top of the brick wall separating our garden from the neighbour's with a Koi carp flapping in his mouth. The proximity of our house to school made it easy for the boys to walk to and fro.

Within six months of our return from America I was appointed as the first full-time cardiac surgeon in Liverpool. The vacancy for a consultant appointment came about unexpectedly. Pat Molloy decided to move to a new job in Victoria Hospital, Belfast, Northern Ireland. A new post of full-time cardiac surgeon was created, initially in the adult team at Broadgreen Hospital. Within two years I had developed a major interest in the surgery of congenital heart defects. Ronald Edwards and John Bickford had performed pioneering work in this field and I was fortunate to be welcomed into their practice. It was clear that cardiac surgery needed development in the adult age-range as well as in the area of children and adults suffering from congenital cardiac defects. New born babies and children under the age of approximately five years presented a particular challenge. Adults requiring valve replacement posed the question,

"What type of valve should be inserted in the place of the existing valve?"

Should they receive a man made prosthetic valve or could a human or animal valve be grafted in the place of the pathological one with long-term success? This type of surgery requires modern operating theatre facilities with temperature and humidity control and availability throughout the week. Patients are then moved to an intensive care ward that is well equipped with appropriate monitoring equipment watched over by fully trained nurses on a twenty four hour basis. During the nineteen sixties and early seventies these facilities were not available in Liverpool in spite of a large intensive care unit, possibly the first to be constructed in this country. The frustration that faced Pat Molloy and subsequently me was created by the lack of intensive care beds that were specifically designated for cardiac surgical patients. The cases for surgery were booked in advance only to be cancelled during the following week if, as was often the case, intensive care beds became filled with cases from the other departments in the hospital. Some of these might require intermittent positive pressure ventilation and the oversight of nurses and anaesthetists.

Like Pat Molloy, I was appointed to a post that lacked the facilities required to carry out a regular program of heart operations without interruption. Ronald Edwards and John Bickford each relinquished one of their three surgical sessions, leaving us each with two sessions per week. Considerably more time was required as we moved into the realm of open heart surgery for infants (under one year of age) and neonates (under one month of age).

I wish to record the support of Ronald Edwards and John Bickford and the consultant anaesthetists with whom I worked for many hours at a time. Dr Gordon Jackson Rees, Dr Alan Stead and Dr Tom Abbott made up a splendid team and the success that was achieved in the unit was in large part possible as a result of their remarkable skills and friendly support.

Gordon Jackson Rees, "Jack," as he was known widely was senior paediatric anaesthetist in Liverpool when I joined the cardio-thoracic surgical team in the early 1970's. Working with Ronald Edwards as surgeon, they pioneered palliative and corrective cardiac surgery with great success. They were supported ably by Dr Alan Stead and Dr Tom Abbott and by John Bickford. Jack took up paediatric anaesthesia after the war (1939-1945) at the suggestion of professor Cecil Grey. Together they worked out the role of the muscle relaxant "curare" in clinical practice. Because the patient is muscularly paralysed, ventilation must be carried out artificially. When this support is needed for long periods of time, gases must be delivered through a system of tubing which cannot be disconnected by the patient. Jack suggested using a naso-tracheal tube which was fixed firmly to the forehead of the patient with a wide band of elastoplast strapping. This made it possible to support a child on a ventilator for three weeks or more and trachyostomy was seldom necessary.

Jack was inspirational to work with, his enthusiasm being infectious. His confidence grew out of his vast clinical experience. This enabled him to appear where he was needed at just the right moment. This was a product of a fertile imagination and his zest for life in his chosen subject.

A visiting consultant anaesthetist from Holland was attending an open heart operation when the team was short staffed. Dr Rees was giving the anaesthetic, maintaining intravenous infusions, administering drugs, now jumping up to adjust the roller pump of the heart lung machine. The visitor was heard to comment,

"This Jackson Rees, he is incredible. He is active in all directions!"

Jack was equal to every challenge. He was an inspiring colleague and a great friend. His contribution to the success of anaesthetic service to children in Liverpool was immense.

Following in the footsteps of Professor John D Hay's enthusiastic foundation of this combined branch of medicine and surgery, were Dr R S Jones and Dr Jean Shackleton. Dr Jones developed an interest in the detailed anatomy of congenital heart conditions. He stimulated important laboratory work with detailed histological demonstration of the anatomical variations that the surgeon has to contend with on the operating table. Before angiography was developed to the high standard that was subsequently achieved, I taught students that like the abdomen in general surgery, the heart can be a "veritable temple of surprises."

Full cardiological investigation prior to surgery includes passing a fine tube into the patient's artery or vein peripherally. This is advanced up to and into the heart. Blood samples are taken from the various heart chambers and the oxygen content of each sample is calculated. Secondly, the pressure in each chamber is recorded. Thirdly, contrast medium is injected under pressure through the catheter. This combination of catheterisation and angiography has been superseded by echo cardiography in recent years. It was necessary in gaining initial experience with these techniques to work on a Saturday afternoon. This was the only time when it was possible for the essential members of the team to meet. John Hay built up a large catchment area in the North West, North Wales and the Isle of Man. He recruited Ronald Edwards and later John Bickford as surgeons. A large experience in palliative and totally corrective operations in children resulted. This included a variety of operations to close holes in the partitions that separate the left and right atria and the two ventricles. They developed wide experience in the surgery of coarctation of the aorta, ductus arteriosus and "blue babies." Ronald Edwards carried out the first Mustard procedure to redirect pulmonary and systemic venous blood flow, inserting an inter-atrial baffle. If necessary, children were cooled to moderate or deep hypothermic temperature. This allowed the surgeon to arrest the heart and occlude all blood flow into the heart for a maximum period of one hour. Longer periods of circulatory rest could result in brain damage. Because of the time limit of sixty minutes accurate data was required by the surgeon from the cardiologist. This gave the surgeon his best chance of effecting a successful repair.

Whilst some congenital defects cause little detriment to the circulation, multiple defects can cause lethal cardiac failure as early as the first weeks of life. Normal life activities may be possible for many years when minor defects only are present. Thus, children with heart defects of a congenital nature may present in the first weeks of life or not until teenage years or even later. In either case the advice of a specialised team will be necessary to supervise the patient's activity and lifestyle.

During the early nineteen seventies the team appreciated this: infants under one year of age and who required help because of a heart condition fell into certain diagnostic groups. At least two thirds of these babies died unless total corrective surgery could be performed successfully. Ronald Edwards received a grant from The British Heart Foundation to investigate the feasibility of performing open heart surgery in babies in the new-born period that weighed only a few kilograms. The surgical mortality was high but on re-examining the investigatory data, it was concluded that the selection of cases for surgery had been inappropriate as several children should have been regarded as inoperable at that time.

"David, you'll have to find another way," stated Ronald Edwards.

The challenge appealed to me and the gauntlet was on the ground.

Discussions with Dr Jackson Rees ensued and we decided to use profound hypothermia by cooling the circulating blood in the patient and in the heart lung machine circuit. A heat exchanger that is built into this machine allowed us to cool the baby's core temperature down to eighteen degrees

Centigrade. The baby's blood volume was drained into the heart lung machine and was kept at low temperature during the next hour. This period of time was given to the surgeon for the completion of any type of repair that he could confidently carry out within the time allotted.

Meticulous care to avoid the entry of air into the child's arterial system was essential. The surgeon now had near perfect conditions in which to operate on a heart barely the size of a Victoria plum. Delicacy was then the order of the day for the surgical team. Some surgeons employed magnification to improve the accuracy of their suturing within the heart. Pleasingly, surgical survival increased dramatically. One specific group of infants whose mortality without surgery was known to be in the order of 85% was found to be permanently correctable if surgery was carried out in the first four weeks of life.

I was appointed to the Mersey Region Health Authority in April 1968. As well as those mentioned, my colleagues were Leslie J Temple, Ken Waddington and Ian Morrison. Each Friday these surgeons would attend a joint case conference with their cardiological colleagues and consultant radiologists. Cases were discussed and their investigations were presented. The selection of cases that were to be operated on in the following week was made during this meeting. The meeting was attended by junior staff and a certain level of teaching was available.

After one of these Friday case conferences I was taken by Dr Norman Coulshed to see a patient who was close to demise. His head was slumped on one side. His lips were blue and he was in terminal cardiac failure. He appeared to me to have but a few days to live.

The name of this patient was Philip Toosey.

Philip Toosey had suffered at the hands of the Japanese when he was interned with many of his men. He found himself appointed as commandant of the prison camp that provided slave labour for the construction of the bridge over the River Kwai. Alec Guinness portrayed Brigadier Toosey in the film depicting the construction of the bridge of the same name. He and several other Japanese POW's who returned to Merseyside after the war later developed leaking Mitral heart valves as a result of their poor diet. He and his family, realising that he was terminally ill, were prepared for him to undergo replacement of his Mitral valve and wanted a surgeon to consider his case. I had some strong feelings of sympathy for his plight as one of my uncles, Dr Edward W Kirk, had been interned by the Japanese in Stanley camp in Hong Kong. He practised surgery in the camp throughout the occupation. I told Philip Toosey's family that we could replace his faulty Mitral valve with a man-made prosthesis but I could not guarantee that his heart would be strong enough to support him during the early recovery period following surgery. I suggested that his chances of surviving the operation were rather less than 50-50. The family went away and discussed the situation in the light of this information. I was asked to carry out replacement of the affected valve. The operation went smoothly and he was transferred to the intensive care unit. At approximately 7am on the following morning, after his operation, he developed cardiac arrest. He was resuscitated quite quickly by a team of resident doctors and nurses led by Mr Ben Meade. The same situation arose during the afternoon of the same day whilst I was visiting him in the intensive care ward. Again, he responded to standard methods of resuscitation. However, he remained desperately ill and developed kidney and liver failure and required continuous monitoring and intensive care for several weeks.

Philip Toosey was transferred to the male ward in the chest unit at Broadgreen. One afternoon, I visited him and after examining him, he said,

"David, what you need in this ward is television sets."

I replied, "You get better, and then I'll tell you what we need here!"

The ITU that served the whole of Broadgreen Hospital was situated in the chest unit. It was a very large ward, having some eighteen beds, but none were dedicated specifically for cardiac patients who had just had their operations. The development of cardiac surgery was delayed as beds that had been reserved for open heart surgery during the following week were frequently required for emergency admissions. These included cases of chest trauma, pneumonia and patients requiring assisted ventilation. Many patients were frustrated because their surgery had been postponed twice or more. When Philip Toosey had recovered sufficiently, I explained this to him and told him that we required £30,000 to make alterations to the ITU. This would mean dividing the ward longitudinally so that one half of the original ward could be set aside as a specialised cardiac recovery unit and the remaining half would serve the rest of Broadgreen Hospital. As soon as he was discharged home he recruited the help of his good friend, Sir Douglas Crawford. Within six months they raised £50,000 by themselves. Additional finance to provide new monitoring equipment for the ward and furnishing for the relative's accommodation was provided by the Area Health Authority. It is a fact that this initiative marked a point of great progress in the history of surgical treatment of heart defects in the Merseyside region. Philip Toosey survived over five years after his operation and he was awarded a knighthood, partly in respect for his role as commandant in a Japanese prison camp, partly for his role as Chairman of The School of Tropical Medicine in Liverpool and partly for his role in supporting cardiac surgery.

During the early nineteen seventies, it became clear that, in Liverpool, the surgery of children suffering from congenital heart defects was in danger of lagging behind the most active units around the world. The Royal Liverpool Children's Hospital, was also affectionately known as Myrtle Street, being situated on the street of that name. They had a very large experience of the more straight-forward and moderately complex heart conditions. John Hay led the investigatory side of the specialised work and there were over two hundred infants and children awaiting surgery in 1970. It was necessary to refer some of the more urgent cases to Dr Fontan in Bordeaux and to Sir Magdi Yakoub at Harefield Hospital in Uxbridge.

It became clear to me that I could not continue to operate on children and adults at hospitals that were separated by several miles of the city. As an extreme example, one might be required at both hospitals simultaneously and this occasionally meant cancelling one of two operations.

In 1974 I became fully committed to the Royal Liverpool Children's Hospital (RLCH). I performed a few operations on adults at Broadgreen Hospital each year until my departure from Liverpool to take up the foundation Chair of cardiac surgery at Edinburgh University in 1987. I remained as the sole consultant cardiac surgeon to the Children's Hospital during the 1970's when the Area Health Authority created a new post for a second full-time paediatric cardiac surgeon. Miss Roxanne McKay was appointed and we shared the work for several years until I left for Edinburgh. Miss McKay brought up to date expertise in modern cardio-respiratory bypass and support from her association with some of America's leading surgeons. Roxanne was totally dedicated to her work and to her patients. With her input we increased the number of patients who passed through the unit each year and we believe we headed the league table of palliative and totally corrective surgical cases per annum in the UK. The mortality figures that had previously been very competitive improved further, particularly in the highly complex group of infants and children over one year of age.

One of the requirements for progress up the surgical ladder is research into the frontiers of a developing subject. This takes time and the demands on the individual surgeon can become considerable. There are different aspects to this part of one's training that can include overcoming clinical problems and the analysis of patients' response to different therapies and treatments. The young surgeon can become involved in the development of products such as instruments and equipment, for example the heart lung machine, before it was made as a disposable unit demanded much thought and experimentation. Doctors are frequently approached by large medical companies who wish to recruit them with specific areas of knowledge that may be of value as they seek to win ground over competitors. Such research based on the cardiac unit at Myrtle Street was invaluable to my own understanding of a complex subject. Continuing research over many years was carried out on children whose operations I had performed. The knowledge obtained from studying the detailed anatomy of the specialised conducting tissue that propagates the heart beat from the filling chambers to the pumping chambers went around the world from our unit. This was worked on by Dr RS Jones, Dr Robert Arnold, Dr James Wilkinson and Dr Audrey Smith. Joining this team from Manchester and later as professor of cardiac morphology at the Brompton Hospital, London was Robert Anderson.

I was able to continue the work I had started in Dr Gerbode's unit in America on my return to Liverpool. I continued to study ways of mounting porcine aortic valves that were sutured into a flexible frame for insertion as a replacement of a damaged Mitral valve. I was also surgeon to a team that included Dr John Wright in testing a totally new design for a prosthesis to replace the Mitral valve that was made out of ceramic material. This was aimed at producing a very thin coating of cells to obviate the necessity for patients requiring anticoagulants. These are necessary for the prevention of clots of blood from forming on prosthetic valves and later detaching to form a small blood clot within the arterial system. The use of pig valves and the design of our ceramic valve prosthesis have both been brought in for commercial use and we were very much in line with the design of these products.

During the early 1970's I was asked by the British Council if I would receive a visiting consultant surgeon from Poland. He worked in Biolystok in eastern Poland, having previously worked in Warsaw. Dr Wagner provided the first link of a ten-year association between RLCH and the Child Health Centre in Warsaw. I set up a Fellowship scheme for young surgeons from countries outside Great Britain using fees from the small number of private patients that I was allowed to treat each year. This was because I was fully committed to the NHS. After Dr Wagner's visit, Myra and I were invited to visit centres in Warsaw and we also made the long journey East to Biolystok by car. The association with Poland worked well and we were able to appoint about eight of their young doctors who were training in chest surgery. Myra and I made annual visits to the Child Health Centre and single visits to Gdansk, Szczecin and Zakopane. In Warsaw I joined in diagnostic discussions and operated on a number of complex and second-time operations.

During my term in office in Edinburgh we received a number of complex cases from Poland. This added to the liaison that was forged with Edinburgh. Many Polish refugees settled in Edinburgh during the war and a Polish School of Medicine was established within Edinburgh University. two hundred and twenty seven Polish students graduated as doctors through the Polish School that used the experience of a number of Polish teachers, augmented by medical staff within the Faculty of Medicine in Edinburgh.

On the day of my interview for the Chair of Cardiac surgery, I was waiting in the University precinct, when I came upon a bronze plaque let into the stone wall. This plaque thanks the Faculty of Medicine in Edinburgh for welcoming the development of a faculty of Polish Medicine and for the cooperation that developed between the two universities. This experience was picked up by one of my interviewers and was a very acceptable topic of conversation on that occasion.

My appointment to the Foundation Chair of cardiac surgery in Edinburgh was exciting. I had links with this magnificent city through my mother who was born and raised in Morningside. My father graduated in civil engineering in the two and a half years following World War 1. He joined the firm of Mott, Hay and Anderson. The population of Scotland is relatively smaller than that in England. The incidence of congenital heart defects presenting in childhood is approximately one case per hundred live births. Therefore the requirement for cardiac surgery was less than I had been accustomed to in Liverpool. I was involved in the surgery of a number of adults, some of whom had had palliative or corrective operations previously. Before the decision had been taken to establish cardiac transplantation in Glasgow we carried out a demanding experimental study. Although it was a disappointment to the team in Edinburgh, the decision was accepted with good grace.

During the autumn of 1987, my youngest son, Ross, and his seventeen year old friend, Neville, completed the walk from John O'Groats to Land's End. This was to raise funds for the British Heart Foundation. The walk was planned carefully over the previous year. Accommodation was reserved, giving a definitive objective for each leg of the journey. Alastair, my third son, provided the back-up resources, driving Ross' beat-up old Citroen Visa. Myra accompanied them on the first stages of the journey as physiotherapist, providing foot-care, in particular. Rocky, our English Sheepdog, made an enthusiastic start to the 800 mile trip, but had to retire and return south because of wear and tear to the pads of his feet.

I was very proud to attend the Forth Road Bridge one afternoon as the two walkers appeared on the bridge over the horizon. I am sure that Ross' grandfather would have been just as proud of Ross' determination to follow in Ian Botham's footsteps. The walkers stayed in several of the hotels used by him as they made their way south. They kept up to schedule throughout the whole walk, averaging 27 miles a day. The main stress on the walkers was psychological, rather than physical. As they approached Land's End, I drove through the night from Edinburgh to join the reception party to greet them at their final destination. I took a short nap in a lay-by in the early hours of the morning. I then found a baker who was prepared to write a congratulatory message on an iced cake. The donation to the British Heart Foundation was received gratefully and could have been larger had we organized more supporters to collect money along the way. Ross asked that the proceeds go towards the purchase of equipment in the intensive care ward at the Royal Liverpool Children's Hospital. Thus ended a wonderful and exhilarating experience for Ross and his brother, Alastair, and their friend, Neville, in their attempts to raise much needed funds for a very worthwhile cause. I was delighted for them firstly, because they completed an extremely arduous task, which they themselves had initiated. And secondly, they continued the tradition that Ian Botham had established some years previously. They did actually meet up with the Great Man in Worcester, whilst he was playing cricket for his county, on their way South to Land's End, and have the photo to boot!

left to right: Sir D Crawford, Lady Toosey, Brig. Sir Philip Toosey, opening Gunner Ward, Broadgreen Hospital, 6th June 1973

World Conference in Auckland.
left to right: Dr. Ed Harris, Mr. J. Drakeley,
David I. Hamilton, Sir Brian Barratt Boyes,
Mr. Sandy Grant, Mr. Leslie Temple, Prof. P.J. Molloy

Testing his nerve -
and his Surgeon's!

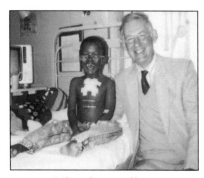

Nigerian smiles

Pantomime Time

Dr. Gordon Jackson Rees

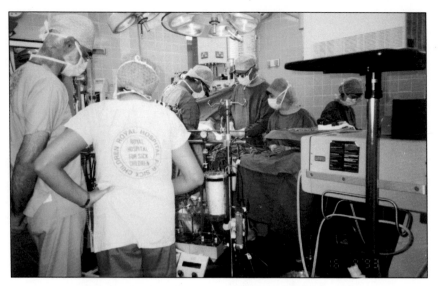

Activity in the Operating Theatre, Edinburgh

Phillipa Lightowler
septation of single ventricle

Andrew Lowe
back to work post-op

"HAPPY IN MY WIFE"
(Quote from John Hunter's Writings)

Myra (nee McAra) was born in Bristol on the 15 of March 1932. Her parents, Revd Malcolm McAra and Marion (nee McDowell) had a son, Geoffrey, who was two years younger than his sister. Myra grew up during her first 6 years in Bristol and Newcastle. For a time she was evacuated to South West Scotland during the war. Her father accepted a call to the Presbyterian Church in Putney in London. The hall and part of the church were demolished in an air raid. During my teens my mother decided to worship as a member of this church and my sister Anne and I joined a few years later. We needed another girl to balance numbers at our Christmas party in 1948. After the party was over Myra accepted my invitation to play golf at Wimbledon Park the next day. She went home with this surprising news and told her mother who exclaimed,

"You didn't say 'Yes' did you?"

Myra's father played to a handicap of 8 and she soon proved that she had inherited some of his golfing genes. She played some excellent shots and for one of the few times throughout our long association of sixty years did as I suggested!

We had quite a lot in common: the countryside and animals. We have delighted in the antics of four Border Terriers who have enriched our family life in many ways. Morag, Bruce, Gemma, Flora, Phoebe (a Golden Labrador) and Rocky, an English sheepdog and a real "gentleman" who had an elegant running action reminiscent of Sebastian Coe at full throttle!

Myra was a good hockey and tennis player and she enjoyed driving, camping and touring. We share a love of music and theatre. She helped our own boys to produce pantomimes in the week before Christmas. We both supervised youth work and Myra was Akela to some 30 cub scouts for several years. This was invaluable experience when our own family arrived. Myra had her hands full in keeping us all together. She frequently played the role of single parent as I became more involved in a demanding branch of surgery. Nearly all my patients passed through the intensive care ward following surgery and this meant that I had to be available unless I was on leave or abroad. For many years I was the sole consultant cardiac surgeon responsible for the operations on children having congenital cardiac defects.

Myra is a skilful dressmaker and an excellent cook. Her latent artistic work in watercolour has brought her recognition in recent years and she has been elected to the Deeside Arts Group. This past three years she has been Chairwoman of the Liverpool University Wives Group, a post she has filled with distinction. Her committee has produced varied, enjoyable and imaginative programmes. She has visited many sites before meetings took place ensuring smooth running on the night and checking that food and facilities were satisfactory.

Myra trained as a physiotherapist at St Mary's Hospital in Paddington. She worked at West Middlesex Hospital, The Middlesex Hospital and ran her own practice in Edinburgh. She carried out evening clinics for athletes at the Commonwealth stadium in Edinburgh. She was a member of the physiotherapy team at Clatterbridge hospital, Wirral. She has ensured that we did not forget that there are other things in life that are important. She has kept an eye on concerts, theatre, poetry readings and on a number of individuals with special needs in the community.

We have travelled far to conferences in many countries. We have had many experiences and a number of adventures as I have attempted to portray.

Times have changed. I probably worked through the best years of the NHS and had magnificent support from my colleagues from many branches of medicine and surgery. Thank you all for joining me on my "Improbable Mission" but I have always believed in "Thunderbolts and Acts of God!" They can turn a man round in the middle of the road.

We all need to find stimulating and satisfying recreation and our family found this together in cruising the inland waterways of England. We owned our own 40 foot narrow boat, "Seth" (meaning "renewal") for fifteen years. Our first exposure to the canal network was in 1953. Our dentist brought to our notice an advertisement in the newspaper put in by the Canal Cruising Company in Stone, Staffordshire. I made a booking for two weeks for the "Angela." She was built in wood and was half of a seventy two foot long working narrow boat powered by a petrol engine. We ordered provisions through the boat yard at Stone by telephone. I remember being impressed when we arrived by train to find on board a large box containing all the items that we had ordered. Myra's aunt Nellie came down from

Wigtownshire for the first week and my father spent a few days with us during the second week. We took to this form of transport immediately. Four miles per hour is one's average walking speed which roughly matches cruising speed on a canal. The varied scenery of countryside and industrial buildings is fascinating. Navigating a narrow boat through a variety of obstacles such as locks, tunnels, over aqueducts and on to rivers and finding suitable moorings are some of the features of canal cruising. The history of the canal system is inextricably bound up with the Industrial Revolution and the development of engineering in this country between 1750 and 1900.

During the early 1970's I suffered my first serious problem with my back. I pulled into a petrol station near Broadgreen Hospital, Liverpool, where I was working as a consultant chest surgeon. I opened the car door but was unable to move due to pain in the lumbar region. This radiated down one leg into the sole of my foot. I spent several weeks on traction in a side ward in the chest unit under Mr Guy Almond, an orthopaedic surgeon. As I recovered, I thought about our holiday on the canals and decided that this could be a splendid way for us to relax together during family holidays. We purchased Seth. She was a modern steel hull narrow boat powered by a Lister diesel engine. There were six bunks, gas cooker and fridge and a shower. Fairly basic compared with modern cruising boats, nevertheless comfortable and giving protection from inclement weather. Our two older boys, were of early teenage years when we purchased Seth. With their two younger brothers, we soon had an expert crew. They would go ahead of the boat, preparing locks and also became excellent navigators themselves.

We kept Seth at a number of moorings over the years. Initially, she lay at Beeston and Bunbury on the Shropshire Union canal, then in Chester and for several years at Lower Heyford on the Oxford canal. Finally, we hired a mooring at the marina near the Anderton Lift, Cheshire. This was an amazing feat of engineering that enabled boats to make the descent from the canal down to the much lower level River Weaver. Seth gave me many challenges over the fifteen years she was in our care. The propeller had not been attached securely and it came off the drive shaft three times. The first time we were unable to retrieve it from the canal. I called on the Liverpool University students scuba club members. They were willing to help. The following weekend, about six of them turned up with underwater illuminating equipment. They retrieved the propeller on their first traverse of the canal and we were soon cruising again. On the other occasions we retrieved the propeller ourselves.

One of our early trips was down the Welsh canal to Llangollen. We were unable to pass through one of the locks at Grindley Brook because the bow of the boat became jammed in the front of the lock as we let water out of the sluice gate. Before we realised what was happening, the boat was tilted up at the bow, but the stern was at a much lower level, still afloat as water rushed out of the lock. Either Seth was too wide across the bow or the lock had caved in somewhat. By fiddling with the water level in the lock and by flushing water through the lock from the canal above we were able to free the boat. The slope on the floor was steep enough to cause the gas stove to slide to the stern at considerable speed! The stove hit my legs with some force but no serious damage occurred.

We drove down in the car to Lower Heyford on the Oxford canal in 1976.

"So you've come to your floating caravan, have you?" said the manager of the boatyard.

"What do you mean?" we replied.

"The boats are all grounded due to the drought," he informed us.

"You can't move her, you'll have to use her as a floating caravan!"

One of our favourite trips was to Stratford upon Avon from Liverpool. Here we could moor in the basin by the side of the Royal Shakespeare Theatre or by the riverbank directly opposite. By rising early and joining the queue we obtained tickets for whatever play was being performed that evening. Seth provided ideal holidays for the whole family. The boys loved fishing, Myra had time to sketch and to read and I was challenged in keeping Seth in working order.

The canal system is a magnificent monument to man's ingenuity and determination in using many skills to solve apparently insurmountable obstacles.

One of the pleasures of the Fellowship scheme that I was able to inaugurate in Liverpool and to continue in Edinburgh, was paying return visits to the home units of some of the Fellows. The family was fortunate to be invited to spend part of the summer holiday in Ancona on Italy's Adriatic coast. Several of the young surgeons who worked under Professor Palminiello in cardiac surgery there worked on our Fellowship programme in Liverpool. We spent most of our three week vacation on the beach and we were loathe to return home. The first part of this journey was by train following the coastline to Venice. We had arranged to stay two nights before flying home. I had calculated how much of our dwindling currency would be required to pay for lodging, food and our bus fares to the airport.

The week leading up to our departure from Ancona produced some very heavy rain and electric storms. Throughout the morning of our departure, the train moved slowly. Myra and I shared a compartment with several Italian women and the four boys occupied the next compartment and were occupied playing chess on a magnetic board. Myra was engrossed in a book that was part of her syllabus for her Open University degree. The train had to proceed with caution as the shingle around the track sleepers had been washed down the embankments in many places. We pulled into a station and the train came to a halt. The clock approached noon. The ladies decided that it was lunchtime. They opened their bags and brought out meat flavoured with garlic, wine and fruit. These meals made up an enviable repast. My salivary glands burst into action and I decided that I was hungry. Looking through the window across the adjacent car park I saw a sign: "Ristorante." The train showed no sign of moving and many passengers were walking up and down the platform to stretch their legs. I made a snap decision to provide lunch for my family. Myra, I surmised, had not registered that the train had come to a standstill. I made a dash across the track out of the station and into the restaurant. I ordered six cheese rolls from the bar tender, adding, "please be as quick as you can." He disappeared into the area behind the bar and came back to the counter with processed cheese enwrapped with pieces of cling film. This made the bartender's task almost impossible. When he had completed four rolls with cheese, my nerves snapped. I put some money on the counter, seized my purchase and dashed out into the car park. I need not have hurried for I saw the back of the rear coach of the train disappearing out of the station and on its way to Venice, still far off to the North. All manner of thoughts flooded through my mind. We were short of cash.

The family must be thinking that I had been kidnapped. 'Was the Mafia strong in this part of Italy,' I wondered? We might never see each other again. 'What advantages and disadvantages would this bring,' I wondered.

Three Italian gentlemen had been watching this developing saga from the far end of the platform. One now ran towards me. He pulled at my sleeve, directing me outside the station and guided me to the first available vehicle. He explained what had happened to the driver who must have received the message for he revved up his engine, shoved me inside, and shot out of the station proceeding at breakneck speed through the open countryside. We might have been at Brands Hatch since he was warming to his task, taking the bends in the road like a Formula 1 veteran. I put my hand on his arm and said, "slowly, slowly!" This only made things worse for he took one hand off the wheel and patted me on the shoulder and exclaimed, "OK, OK, me Fangio!"

I began to lose my cool, and became convinced that I should not see my family again. I put up a prayer. Suddenly, he made a lightning turn into a station yard. There in front of us was a train that looked somewhat familiar. The driver took what money I could afford to give him and pushed me up the nearest steps into a compartment from which emanated the strong smell of garlic. Myra was sitting as I had left her, possibly an hour earlier, still deep in her book. What concentration! No wonder she passed her degree examination.

"Here you are, I've brought you some lunch."

I handed her a portion of her frozen sandwich, apologizing for its poor condition. I retreated somewhat sheepishly into the next compartment, thinking that surely one of the boys had noticed that I was missing.

"I thought you might be ready for a bite. This is all I could find for lunch."

"Wow, Dad, that looks nice, you could have brought it earlier!"

Sometimes I wonder if it's better to be appreciated or to be ignored. Oh, well, a heart surgeon has to be ready for anything, doesn't he?! The background to our next experience revolves around our shortage of Italian currency. In the warmth of the evening sun on the final night of our epic holiday, we decided to visit St Marks square for coffee. Foolishly, we chose one of the more expensive cafes. A small orchestra was playing in the open air on this balmy night. Tables and chairs were arranged invitingly. Fortunately we selected a table that was quite a long way from the restaurant to which it was attached. I ordered six large cappuccinos without thinking of the consequences. I noticed however, that the waiters serving the guests of the outdoor tables took some time to come out of the cafeteria with their trays heavily laden. Our coffee arrived after some delay, the bill being folded in two. When I surveyed its contents I think my heart missed several beats. The cost was approximately £30. I said nothing to the family but planned our next moves. We were being fleeced! Under the circumstances, we had to take evasive action. I told the family that they had just drunk the most expensive mug of coffee they were ever likely to consume. I suggested the following plan of action: one by one, at suitable intervals, the boys and their mother were to slip away unobtrusively into the night. I stayed in my seat and calculated what meagre contribution towards this unbelievable total I could afford to make. I left my few remaining Lire on the table and slipped back to our hotel.

In 1982, Myra completed a four year degree course with the Open University. She received her degree in English Literature in the McEwan Hall in Edinburgh. At much the same time she was awarded the Bronze Medal by the Royal Society of Prevention of Cruelty to Animals for the successful rescue of Gemma, one of our Border Terriers from a frozen reservoir in the Pentland Hills outside Edinburgh. Gemma had walked out some forty yards on ice that was unable to bear her weight. She found running water draining towards a culvert. Gemma was swimming strongly but hypothermia began to set in causing stiffness and lack of power in her limbs. Myra's instinct was to wade into the water and bring her out. She achieved this in courageous fashion but the water was by now up to her armpits. Myra carried Gemma to safety. I wonder how many of us would have done that? The next week I wrote a citation and sent it to the RSPCA with a covering letter, saying that I wanted the society to know that the events that I described took place one afternoon of the previous week. I was immensely proud to receive a letter a few weeks later saying that the Bronze Medal was awarded relatively infrequently.

What of our four sons?

Ian was born in 1959. He was educated at Kingsmead Preparatory School in Hoylake, as were his three brothers. Ian won an art scholarship to Leighton Park School in Reading, and with James received a Quaker education, following their grandfather and father before them. Ian gained two degrees in interior design and got valuable experience in this field. He established his own business, firstly with "Omnis," an architectural and design company based in London, and then with his own property development firm, also in London. Recently he married Tricia Correa. He has his own band. They perform concerts on request where they play their own compositions. He maintains his enjoyment of tennis. He has become a father in the past month or so, a fifth grandchild for Myra and me.

James was born in 1960. He went to the same preparatory and public schools as Ian. He played rugby and tennis and entered Birkenhead School Sixth form and then went on to Middlesex Hospital Medical School in London, like his father in this respect. All four boys played golf, initially on nine-hole golf courses in South West Scotland. James continues playing with a single-figure handicap. He, following a strong family tradition graduated MB, BS, trained in surgery up to registrar level. He decided to take up general practice and is now a senior partner in a group of General Practitioners South of Nottingham. He is married to Katrina Brien who grew up outside Perth, Scotland. James has continued his interest in golf since his son, Scott, now aged 11 years, is playing to a handicap of 12. He has just been selected to represent the North East of England in his age group. This national competition will be played towards the end of the summer. James and Katrina's daughter, Esme, is also a keen golfer, but has many interests besides.

Alastair entered Birkenhead School from preparatory school and obtained a degree in geography. He is a strong tennis player and was an intimidating fast bowler at cricket. He is married to Iveta, from Riga in Latvia. They first met aboard the missionary ship "Anastasis" where the two of them continued to serve for a short time. They then returned to Europe to get married, eventually in Stockholm in the early 1990's. Iveta is an accomplished dressmaker and homemaker. Alastair enjoys writing poetry and has written on a wide variety of subjects.

Ross developed his natural talent for cricket and scored three centuries before the age of eleven. His off drive, playing against The Leas School, in Hoylake would have satisfied Peter May by virtue of timing and gracefulness. He is a natural golfer playing to a single figure handicap. He trained at Sheffield University, obtaining his degree in sports studies, hoping to enter sports administration. To gain experience however, he joined Lombard Bank and is still with them eighteen years later. He is married to Helen John who overcame the development of Hodgkin's Lymphoma. She is a community nurse. Their sons, Jake and Morgan, are both keen sportsmen and athletes. Jake is a talented actor and has ability at cricket too. They live in Surrey in a picturesque village not far from Gatwick airport.

As I grow older, having developed Parkinson's disease soon after my retirement in 1993, I am conscious of how richly I have been blessed in my family. I am happy to hand the torch of life to them for safekeeping. I do not expect them to perform missions that are impossible. My hope is that they will develop the talents that God has given them to somewhere near their full potential. Nothing "succeeds like success," my mother told me and, "anything that is worth doing is worth doing well," was my father's teaching. The demands of life can be very great and we need a counsellor and a guide who is wiser than us by far. The line must be drawn between humility and arrogance. The step below arrogance on the ladder of life is confidence. This comes from diligent practice in sport, in music, and art or academic pursuits and a host of other activities. The step below confidence is humility, an essential quality that the human race is in danger of losing. Competition has become so intense in most spheres of life and personal ego has taken precedence over a realisation that we cannot do it all by ourselves. As I continue to grow older, I see that Man is a tripartite creature (body, mind and spirit), who requires to worship his God and creator. Each man should decide for himself what form of worship suits him best. Whatever this may be, listening to the still, small voice that is within all of us, has served me well and has enabled me to accomplish my three boyhood ambitions of a mission that seemed improbable at the outset.

Forth Road Bridge 1964

Nev and Ross

Edinburgh Royal Infirmary

Myra and Gemma
Bronze Medal R.S.P.C.A.

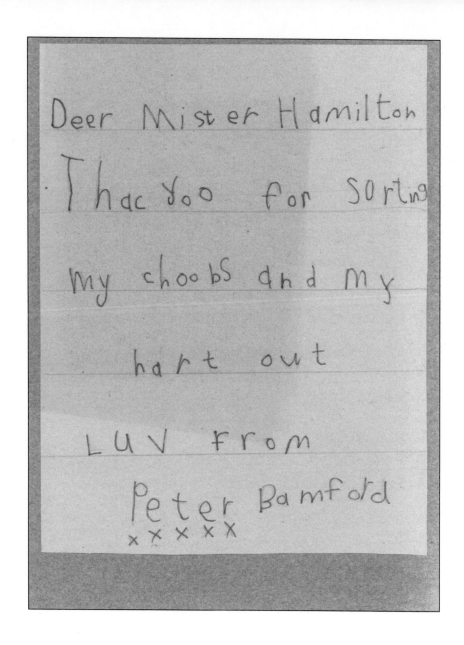

Deer Mister Hamilton

Thac Yoo for sorting

my choobs and my

hart out

LUV From

Peter Bamford
x x x x x

Thank You!

Narrow boat "Seth". Harecastle Tunnel

Lightowler boat "Hamilton"

APPENDIX

The appendix contains material that has never previously been published that may nevertheless be of interest to readers of this book.

My Presidential address to the Society of Cardiothoracic Surgeons of Great Britain and Ireland, York, March 1993:

"ATTRIBUTES REQUISITE IN A SURGEON"

The title of my presidential address is taken from a chapter-heading in Professor Ian Aird's fascinating book, "The Making of a Surgeon," that was published by Butterworth in 1961. This subject has always interested me and is of relevance to each one of us, whatever our specialist skills within the context of cardiothoracic surgery happens to be.

"Attributes" are qualities ascribed to a person or thing. They are "characteristics" that are recognized as appropriate. For example, the human attribute, "humility", is nurtured by all of us, and is, I am sure we would all agree, particularly associated with cardiothoracic surgery. To remind you of this if it should be a new concept for you, the story of Mr Snooks comes to mind. On his first day as Senior House Officer, he was assisting his senior chief with the operation of gastrectomy. No word had passed between the chief and his junior assistant throughout a lengthy operation list. The clock was approaching seventeen hundred hours. The junior SHO suspected that the consultant had not noticed that he had a new assistant working with him. He therefore plucked up courage and posed a question to his boss,

"Who in your estimation, Sir, are the two finest gastrectomists in the world?"

A long pause ensued and the consultant continued to concentrate on suturing the wound. He put down his instruments and gave the SHO a hawk-like gaze over his mask,

"It's a funny thing you should ask me that, Mr Snooks, I can never remember that other fellow's name!"

The time honoured attributes that are requisite in a surgeon are:
"the heart of a lion, the eye of an eagle, and the hand of a lady."
Let us look at these attributes more closely.

Why the lion? He is the ruler of the animal kingdom by virtue of strength, courage, stealth that includes patience and delicacy, by skill, speed of action and ruthlessness. He has great determination, self-confidence and decisiveness of mind. The lion's energy is inexhaustible and sustained. As leader of all the animals in the kingdom, his arrogance must be tempered with humility. A surgeon must express no loss of faith in his own opinion and ability, no vacillation of mind. He should look to the future with optimism and must not allow himself to become downcast by the changing circumstances of life.

The surgeon's life is a burden of constant action, woven through with tragedy. He must accept full responsibility for another's life or death. Sadly, this situation may arise all too often if he is pushing the academic and practical skills of his trade to the limit. The intellectual requirements are exacting and at times rest heavily on a surgeon's shoulders. These requirements are best expressed by Rudyard Kipling in his poignant poem "If,"

"If you can keep your head when all about you are losing theirs and blaming it on you,

If you can trust yourself when all men doubt you, but make allowance for their doubting too;

If you can meet with triumph and disaster and treat these two imposters just the same,

Or watch the things you gave your life to, broken, and stoop and build them up with worn out tools.

If you can fill the unforgiving minute with sixty seconds worth of distance run, yours is the earth, and everything that's in it,

And which is more, you'll be a man my son!"

The surgeon must excel or at the least be thoroughly proficient in clinical medicine and surgery and in counselling his patients whether they be children or adults. He must teach students on their various courses. This may include medical students, nurses, radiographers, physiotherapists and at times, research workers. A consultant surgeon is required to administrate his team efficiently, raise funds and to publish original work in leading medical Journals. He should be aware of the saying, "publish or perish." You may decide, understandably, that this is enough for a single individual to tackle. Rightly or wrongly the majority of surgeons marry and this usually means fathering several children. This leads to a lifelong tug-of-war between professional life and the family's requirements. Any man needs to develop some extra curricular activities to insure that his physical and spiritual batteries are recharged on a regular basis.

The wider our interests and experience of life, the more valuable is the counsel to our patients as we can relate to their needs more completely. A human being is a composite being, and the component parts of his body, mind and spirit must all be addressed before surgery is undertaken. It is through counselling that the patient has opportunity to become familiar with the surgeon, into whose hands the patient is giving himself for a life or death operation. If properly handled, patients begin to recover from the day of pre-operative counselling that should be undertaken by a senior rather than a junior member of the team. Counselling bereaved parents is never easy, neither does it become easier with the passage of time.

Neither do I suppose that any of us who have never experienced such a loss can appreciate fully the emotional avalanche that is created by such an event.

George Barlow, born in 1847, expressed the death of a child starkly.

THE DEAD CHILD

But yesterday she played with childish things,
With toys and painted fruit.
Today she may be speeding on bright wings
Beyond the stars! We ask. The stars are mute.

But yesterday her doll was all in all;
She laughed and was content.
Today she will not answer, if we call;
She dropp'd no toys to show the road she went.

But yesterday she smiled and 'ranged with art
Her playthings on the bed.
Today and yesterday are leagues apart!
She will not smile today, for she is dead.

The Eye of an Eagle

Visual acuity varies enormously from person to person. Modern optics and magnification come to the aid of the less fortunate, as we grow older. To quote professor Ian Aird, " it is in a broader sense that the surgeon's vision should be aquiline." The cardiothoracic surgeon must develop intense, prolonged, unremitting concentration of visual and mental alertness that may have to continue hour after hour. These qualities are already developed in some surgeons from an early age. Evidence of this could be in academic achievements in school, or developed skills in painting, music, chess, bridge or in sport. The surgeon should be aware what is happening around him, particularly in the operating room. He needs to develop the knack of timing, of being in "the right place at the right time."

Anticipation comes with experience.

The Hands of a Lady

It is pleasing to speculate that all surgeons should possess exquisite manual dexterity and technical skill, hands floating artistically over the incision, tissues coming together without tension and in perfect apposition. Our hands have a sensory capacity as well as motor ability. It is the development of this sensory capability in handling immature tissues and those infiltrated with and invaded by pathological processes that distinguish the "Master Craftsman" from the "journeyman surgeon." This skill is part inborn, but can, with constant thought and practice, germinate and mature with experience. The hand's sensory perception is also employed in the physical examination of the patient. This clinical skill is required particularly when the surgeon is examining the acute abdomen.

A surgeon's responsibilities increase as he or she grows older and the demands of our professional lives crowd in on us, at times threaten to overwhelm us. How are we to survive? Not briefly, but over an expected span of forty years from graduation to retirement. The answer is, partly by stealth, by keeping a steady nerve, partly by giving some thought to the matter and partly by God's grace. Putting this another way, by recognizing that we are triangular men and women. For we all possess a body, a mind and a spiritual or emotional dimension.

Just as the make-up of a surgeon can be considered under three headings, our composition as human beings divides into three interrelated parts, Health and happiness, confidence leading to achievement, something in reserve to offer others all stem from a stable state of equilibrium when our personal triangle is in fact isosceles; when the three sides of our being are in balance with each other. Time does not permit the full development of this theme. Suffice it to say that we can respect and develop our physical bodies to very high levels of achievement in professional skills and in the pursuit of our hobbies and in the way we spend our leisure time, or we can abuse them in a number of ways. Our minds and intellects likewise have the potential for great feats. How many of us discipline and train this part of our being? Our minds should control our physical and emotional reactions. Is this always the case?

What about the spirit? Not wishing to preach a sermon, and not wishing to turn you into a congregation, allow me to replace the word "spirit" by enthusiasm. This comes from the Greek word, "enthos" which means possessed by a God, "ardent zeal." If the physical and intellectual attributes of individual humans fall within certain standard deviations our enthusiasm varies greatly and even undergoes diurnal variation to an extraordinary degree for no very obvious reason. How can we nurture and refresh our enthusiasm (spirit) and maintain a vigorous approach to life day-by-day?

Firstly by recognizing that our enthusiasm or spirit is an integral part of our make-up. It needs regenerating on a regular and recurring basis. Adequate rest in sleep and a change of environment revives the flagging sense of humour wonderfully and recharges a flat battery. Some believe that "God breathed into man's nostrils the breath of life, and man became a living soul." Others deny this relationship. Some find solace and refreshment in nature and all her wonderful manifestations and glory. Others find music, art, literature or poetry stimulating. What is certain is that we all have need of "a strong spirit" to give us resilience in times of trouble or disappointment. Make no mistake these times come to all of us if not sooner, then later. We require to find out as individuals, how best we can renew our strength.

One defence mechanism that I have employed successfully in recent years is to select my priorities each day and then to concentrate on the job in hand, diminishing the image of the hundred and one other things that cry out for attention at that time. I say "diminish the image" of the other things, relegating them to the subconscious level, rather than ignoring them completely, because the human mind has a wonderful capacity to handle information at a subconscious level whilst we are busy dealing with the major issues of the moment.

A second defence mechanism is recognition that a team approach is stronger than an individual's effort. Thus we should encourage others, trust others, acknowledge them and respect them. As we become older and our teachers and heroes move on we sometimes miss their support and advice. To whom should we turn?

Shakespeare reminds us that we have "enthos," a spirit or a conscience. Polonius, addressing Laertes, when he is leaving home for France, in Hamlet Act I scene III, gives us some sensible and useful counsel, "neither a borrower, nor a lender be, for loan oft loses both itself and friend, and borrower dulls the edge of husbandry. This above all, to thine own self be true, and it must follow as the night the day, thou cans't not then be false to any man."

I have chosen to share these thoughts with you as they have helped to sustain me during the past thirty five years as a surgeon. It has been a time of rapid and rewarding development in our subject. I have experienced great satisfaction from the challenge in my work. Much of this feeling has come from following patients who have benefited from modern developments in Cardiac Surgery. Surgery has advanced pari passu with the investigatory skills of our colleague cardiologists and the great expertise of the specialist anaesthetists. We must not forget the morphologists who have contributed to our knowledge of the distribution of the specialised conducting tissue within the heart in association with a wide collection of anatomical defects.

It has been an honour and privilege to serve as your President during the past year. I thank you all for your support and for your daily endeavour to maintain the highest standards of our profession.

I particularly wish to thank the members of the executive committee of the Society and the office bearers who have maintained their stalwart effort on your behalf throughout another year.

May God give each one of you strength and wisdom to continue "the tasks to which you have set your hands until they be thoroughly finished:" for this is the vocation of a surgeon.

ADDRESS GIVEN AT BROADGREEN HOSPITAL, LIVERPOOL ON JUNE 6TH 1973 on the OCCASION OF THE OPENING OF THE INTENSIVE THERAPY UNIT FOLLOWING ITS REDEVELOPMENT.

The ward had been partitioned into two to give beds specifically reserved for the post operative care of patients following cardiac surgery.

My Lord Mayor and Lady Mayoress, Chairman of the Hospital Management Committee, Professor Gray, Sir Douglas Crawford, Brigadier and Mrs Philip Toosey, guests and friends. It is my privilege and pleasure as Chairman of the Division of Cardiothoracic Surgery, to express our gratitude to Brigadier Toosey, to Sir Douglas Crawford and to their many friends for the provision of a much needed post operative intensive care ward for the regional service in cardiac surgery. Those of you who have visited the ward will have seen what has been achieved with your support.

For the first time in this unit, we have beds that are specifically reserved for patients recovering from major heart surgery. For the first time since open heart surgery was first performed regularly in this hospital in 1964 our work in this field can continue smoothly without interruption.

Not only have you enabled us to build this ward, but you have equipped it throughout with completely new furnishings, beds of advanced design, and the best electronic patient-monitoring equipment that is currently available. Furthermore, the adjacent intensive therapy ward for the hospital has been upgraded and re-equipped to present day requirements with specific improvements aimed at minimising cross infection between patients.

It is understandable that this is a day of great exhilaration throughout the whole of Broadgreen Hospital. For this we thank you all with genuine sincerity.

The rebuilding of this ward, like the building of a famous bridge on the Burma Railway has not been a simple task. Obtaining agreement and hierarchical support, with temporary ward closures and emergency working conditions over a period of eighteen months, were frustrating and included industrial strikes, delays, rising costs and VAT!

I can only mention some of the many who have joined in making this enterprise possible. This is an opportunity to thank Sir Douglas Crawford, and other individual donors for all their contributions. Mr Ralph Whitehead and the Merseyside Hospitals Council have generously donated new furnishings for the ward. The British Heart Foundation have donated half of the patient monitoring equipment. The Liverpool Regional Hospital Board have added a large sum of money to complete the building costs and have also supplied many additional items of equipment. Their architects designed and supervised the scheme successfully.

I wish to thank Mr Geoffrey Bateson, group Secretary of the East Liverpool University Hospital Management Committee for his unfailingly cheerful and optimistic support at all times. Mr Frank Inman, not with us today and Mr John Watson have performed stalwart work in coordinating and organising this opening ceremony. Mr Bott, the general contractors manager, deserves our particular thanks for, at times, he appears to have carried on the work of rebuilding virtually single-handed.

I also wish to thank my Surgical and Medical colleagues at all levels and the nursing staff who have born the exigencies of the days of rebuilding with the greatest patience and helpfulness. Miss Pat Ashworth and Dr JC Richardson, in particular, have given generously of their time and energy, ensuring that our requirements have been met as far as is possible within this scheme.

Most of you here today will know in essence how this ward came to be rebuilt. Some of you have been privileged to know the man who has enabled us to achieve this. He came here three and a half years ago when he was desperately ill. He was a man whose outstanding qualities of character and leadership were legendary. It has been said that it was surprising that he survived the operation, but he had survived before and the same qualities that inspired thousands of men who were inhumanely imprisoned under the most appalling conditions were essential for his own recovery.

He knows that he suffered two cardiac arrests on the day following surgery. Teamwork of the highest order enabled him to recover.

To the senior British Officer in the camp who once leapt between a fellow officer and the advancing point of a Japanese bayonet these were only temporary setbacks. Here is a unique man. In his earliest days of recovery from a most critical illness, he was still able to recognise that a lack of facilities constituted a serious restraint to providing an efficient regional service for patients requiring heart surgery.

In thanking you for this magnificent ward complex, we are conscious of the trust that you have expressed in us at Broadgreen Hospital. It is fitting that you have given us bricks and mortar and our tools of trade. You have also shown us the spirit in which we must endeavour to work.

We wish you and your wife who sustained you so valiantly throughout your long illness every happiness for days to come. We at Broadgreen shall always remember you and your inspiring achievements in sickness and in health. We shall draw heavily on this source of strength to ensure that your ward, Gunner Ward, serves the men and women of this great city with distinction and devotion, indeed, just as you have done.

It is my very great pleasure to present to you this token of affection and esteem from all of us at Broadgreen Hospital. The Crusader mounted on this silver paper knife bears his own message to you far more poignantly than any words of mine can express.

Authors note: The opening of Gunner Ward proved to be a turning point in the development of cardiac surgery for adults in the North West of England and it has surpassed its objectives over the years since 1973.

ADDRESS TO THE POLISH ASSOCIATION OF PAEDIATRIC SURGEONS AT THE SEVENTH CONGRESS HELD IN SZCZECIN.

Early links with Poland during the Second World War.

The gathering storm in Europe in the late 1930s erupted in 1939. The attack on Poland was launched on the first of September, followed seventeen days later by the invasion of Russia in the East. Your country was occupied and divided. But Poland did not accept defeat.

Thousands of Polish people fled the country, many reaching France and Britain. Rather than dwelling on the appalling atrocities and barbarism that followed, the attempts of the conquerors to break the spirit of a nation, I wish to remember one of the small ways in which those emigrant people began to recreate their spirit and their country.

Lt. Colonel Professor FAE Crew, a member of the Faculty of Medicine was Commanding Officer of the military hospital at Edinburgh castle. He was a man of vision and was aware of the presence of a considerable number of medical students in the Polish Forces. There were also some professors and lecturers in medical faculties in their own country. Professor Crew conceived the idea of establishing a medical faculty at the University of Edinburgh so that these students could be taught by their own teachers in their own language. A final agreement between the Polish government and the University of Edinburgh was signed on the 24th of February in 1941, creating a Polish Medical School within the University.

The aim of the medical school was two fold: a) to supply qualified doctors to the armed services and, b) to prepare a body of doctors for a liberated Poland.

The medical school was an independent Polish academic institution attached to the university that provided all necessary clinical and laboratory facilities for the conduct of medical teaching. The faculty consisted of Polish professors who had held chairs in Poland and of British and other professors of the Faculty of Medicine of Edinburgh University. Examinations were conducted in Polish or in English.

136

The principal and vice-chancellor of the university, Sir Thomas Holland said, two years later,

"In the beginning we considered the creation of the Polish School of Medicine, as an experiment. Now we can testify that the experiment was successful, and now we will be friends forever."

By 1945, there were ten professors and twenty seven senior lecturers. Research was conducted and about one hundred papers published. In 1944-5 two hundred and twenty students attended the school. The last group of students attained their diplomas in 1949. The school had a lifespan of eight years. Eighteen students received MD diplomas after submitting a thesis.

In 1977 I received a request from the British Council in London asking me to accept a Polish surgeon who was interested in the surgery of congenital heart disease at the Royal Liverpool Children's Hospital. Dr Alexander Wagner arrived and observed our team in action After his return to Poland he introduced me to the officers of the Polish Association of Paediatric Surgeons who invited my wife and myself in 1978. We visited Warsaw, Poznam and Biolystok.

In Poznam we were entertained by Professor Wojtowicz in the department of paediatric surgery. He entertained us to a memorable meal at one of his favourite restaurants outside the city. We had a very happy time with him and it was a real sadness to hear of his death a few years later. When he was showing us around his city, we had to shelter from a heavy rainstorm in the cathedral. We were greatly impressed by the "gold chapel." The drive across Poland from West to East to visit Dr Wagner's clinic in Biolystok was another memorable experience.

In Warsaw we visited the old city recently reconstructed to how it was before it was largely destroyed by invaders. We made our first visit to the Child Health Centre and to the Opera.

As a result of this visit, I was asked to take Dr Andyrzej Cedro for a year's training in paediatric cardiac surgery in Liverpool in 1979. This was made possible by the support of the National Heart Research Fund in the North of England. This is a charitable organisation that raises money for research and training in cardiac surgery. It was possible for five young

Polish surgeons in training at the Child Health Centre in Warsaw to spend a year each at the Royal Liverpool Children's Hospital.

The second to come was Krzysztof Ebinger in 1981. The third was Zigmunt Kalicinski Jnr in 1985. The fourth was Bohdan Maruszewski and recently, Peotr Burczynski. He was able to come with me to Edinburgh for the later part of his Fellowship when I was appointed professor of cardiac surgery in 1987.

Other Polish visitors to Liverpool cardiac surgical units include Dr Stan Barciezowski of Lodt, Dr Maria Hancowicz, Professor Jaroslav Stodulski, Dr W A Kaminski, Dr Wanda Kawalec in 1980 and Dr Joanna Szynkiewicz Dangel in 1986.

During the past ten years my wife and I have visited Poland every year once and sometimes twice. We have been the guests of your association and have been supported by the British Council. We have enjoyed kind and generous hospitality from many people. One year we followed your Sea Cadets training ship, the Dan Moisevitch, from Liverpool to Gdynia, and were entertained by her crew in both ports at a short time interval.

I have been privileged to follow David Waterston at Great Ormand Street Hospital in London as "unofficial advisor" to some of your cardiac teams. Perhaps the honour that you have bestowed upon me in making me a member of PAPS at this meeting makes my role an official one.

It has been a great experience to make these visits to your country, to work with you and to operate on some of your children with congenital heart defects. I owe special thanks to Professor Irena Gizycka and to Professor Krystina Wysocka at Litewska Street Clinic. I thank Professor Jaroslav Stodulski at Centrum for his friendship and warm welcome and to Professor Irena Smolska, chief of the Second Medical Academy Clinic in Warsaw.

However brilliant the individual players may be, the orchestra needs a conductor! All of our visits and movements in Poland have been orchestrated by Professor Zygmunt Kalicinski whose energy, enthusiasm and organisational ability needs no qualification from me. One of the happiest features of these visits has been that my wife has been able to accompany me and as a physiotherapist she has visited Rehabilitation Centres and supports the work of Sue Ryder.

Professor Kalicinski and I have, for several years, discussed how we could organise surgery for some Polish children with complex congenital malformations in Liverpool or in Edinburgh. Offers of help, financial help, have been made, but there are difficulties in shortage of facilities within the British Health Service. Now that I have moved to Edinburgh, I may be in a position to offer help in this direction.

Because he has an uncle and aunt in Lancashire in the North of England the parents of six year old Mateus Krolik of Konin were able to come to Edinburgh recently to see whether he was suitable for major heart reconstruction. We confirmed that surgery was possible and carried out a successful operation. In seeking for accommodation for doctor Burczyinski and his family when they visited Edinburgh, I was introduced to the widow of a Polish man and her daughter, Maria. They have an apartment in their house which is near the Children's Hospital that they are prepared to offer to the parents of any Polish children who come to Edinburgh for surgery. More than this, Maria, who is a doctor, has asked me to announce the establishment of a scholarship in memory of her father which she will finance each year. This award will be made to a young doctor, surgeon or anaesthetist to enable them to visit Edinburgh and to work with our team throughout the period of the association with the patient's hospitalisation in Edinburgh.

These gestures of friendship and good will have increased my resolve to organise this opportunity for some Polish children to receive cardiac reconstruction in Edinburgh. Th establishment of this link would surely be a practical expression of the friendship that has existed between our countries, that flourished through the Polish Medical School in Edinburgh during the war years and that has existed in our own visits to your country.

This expression of "good will" between our countries is only possible because of the sacrifice of those who went before us. This is a small repayment of the debt we owe to those whose spirit could not be broken when the storm gathered around them.

The Following address was given to the congregation gathered in Birkenhead School Chapel on the 24th February in 1980.

"THE HEART OF THE MATTER"

We all enjoy receiving cards at Christmas and letters throughout the year. Some bring messages that we can share with others but some are very personal and private. I have been asked to tell you about my work as heart surgeon to the Royal Liverpool Children's Hospital, which serves the North West of England, the Isle of Man and North Wales. In particular, I shall tell you about the philosophy that sustains me day by day and year by year in a demanding and exacting professional life. I have decided to open my post bag this evening and to share with you some of its secrets which are the rewards of my work.

The first card is from Laura.

"I don't suppose you remember me," she writes. " I came into Liverpool's Children's Hospital in May 1978. I want to thank you a million times. I am now playing for the school's netball team, staying at gym club, going to Girl Guides and I have just completed a First Aid test at St John's Ambulance Brigade, for I have joined them as well. Thanks again for the heart operation."

What are heart operations as far as children are concerned?

Eight of every thousand live born babies have a heart defect due to abnormal development during the first few weeks of life in the womb. These defects vary from holes in the inside partitions of the heart to abnormalities of valves and more complex problems where the main arteries arise from the wrong pumping chambers. Some hearts have as many as seven associated defects and require major reconstructions, using artificial tubes and valves. These operations can take five or six hours to complete. Operations to make blue children pink are amongst the most satisfying of all surgical procedures.

These operations are exercises in team work demanding high professional standards from as many as fifty people including surgeons, doctors, anaesthetists, nurses, radiographers and technicians in many departments.

What is the success rate and are there failures?

Enormous strides have been made in the last decade. At our hospital almost 90% of heart operations carried out on children of all ages each year are successful and many go on to live normal, active lives and have normal or near normal life expectancy. Sadly, we fail in 10-12% of cases and these are usually under predictable circumstances. 85-90% of babies with certain types of heart defect will die before their first birthday without corrective surgery. However, death sometimes comes unexpectedly as a profound shock.

How do we handle this situation which might so easily shake our confidence and weaken our resolve?

Surgical failure must be balanced against the natural history or course of the heart condition untreated. In Liverpool, we have pioneered the corrective heart surgery of babies under one year of age during the past ten years. The success rate has been about 75% in 200 babies under one year of age who have undergone surgery since 1970. We discuss the problems with the parents as fully as we can before all high risk operations and I see all parents after each open heart operation, whatever the time of the clock, to give them a complete account of what we have done and what this should achieve as the child grows up in the future.

I believe that this is the best way to handle fellow human beings through times of crisis. By personal contact, anticipation, explanation, understanding and complete honesty it is possible to build a strong rapport with the families concerned. This is borne out in the next card I received last year from the parents and brother of a little girl called Rachel. Sadly, she did not survive a second heart operation.

"The loss of Rachel was a shattering blow for you, as it was for us. Your devotion, kindness, and in particular, your complete truthfulness over Rachel's illness over the past six years has helped us now to reach the state of inner peace."

So we care about the children who are our patients. We study their heart conditions very carefully and strive to improve our skills and knowledge year by year, to bring more and more previously inoperable conditions into the correctable group.

But why? What motivates us? Is it just professional pride or a thirst for reputation and achievement?

In attempting to answer this question, I want us to consider what factors influence the sort of person we grow up to be. I think there are three important ones.

First, there are genetic, familial characteristics inherited from our parents. These decide our physical make up, our body build, any speech idiosyncrasies and even, perhaps, familial illnesses, our intellectual capabilities, our talent for art, music, science and sports. All these are transferred by two cells, the egg and the sperm which is one of the miracles of creation.

Secondly, our environmental factors, things going on around us day by day. These apply particularly during the first years of our lives up to the age of seven or perhaps twelve years. Our home environment, our parent's attitudes, the influence of grandparents and our brothers and sisters all have an influence on our own "make up." Our school teachers are important in this respect as are church connections and the influence of clubs and special activity groups if we join them.

Thirdly, there are "thunderbolts and acts of God." We cannot insure our houses against these eventualities which may strike us down inexplicably. Such events may, of course, work in our favour. Illness brings us time to reflect, to rest and to take stock of events and we are able to recharge our batteries with renewed energy. St Paul's experience on the road to Damascus was an act of God which revolutionised his life. My own parents had a profound influence on the development of my character and on my beliefs. My father left Bootham Quaker School at the age or seventeen and went out to France as an ambulance driver during the First World War. He qualified as a civil engineer at Edinburgh University and joined Mott, Hay and Anderson's team of civil engineers who specialised in the building of tunnels and bridges in England and overseas. He was a fine craftsman in wood and metal and supported the Second World War effort through a precision engineering business that he established in our garden in Wimbledon. Three full time craftsmen and several part timers made up the work force. During the London blitz he preferred to sleep in his bed trusting in God's protection which had seen him through the horrors of the First World War in France. He received the George medal from King George VI for leading a bomb disposal team in West London who were confronted by 1,000KG unexploded German bomb. This was in danger of destroying the nearby gasworks and other instillations in the area. He brought me up in his workshop by example and I passed school certificate (O Level) woodwork with distinction. His teaching made it easier to train as a surgeon.

From my mother I learned about the church and medicine, music and golf, and the sadness of death in childhood. She was the daughter of an Edinburgh manse (vicarage) one of seven children. One of her brothers, my uncle, died at an early age after suffering kidney disease throughout his teens. Two more brothers were surgeon missionaries in South China and they started the first nurses training school there. My mother was a missionary nurse and midwife in Syria before she married my father. She taught me that it is people and not possessions nor money that matter most. She was a fine judge of character and took great delight in observing human nature in action. She looked through compassionate eyes with a sharp sense of humour.

It was as a boy of twelve when working at the lathe one day that I determined to be a surgeon. My ambition was to combine medicine with manual skills. That this schoolboy dream actually materialised was due to the third determinant of our characters: "acts of God." Throughout the teenage years a lot of my time was spent on sport and rebuilding motorbikes and later, cars, when I was older. Golf, cricket, rugby and tennis were played to a sufficiently high standard to enable me to understand that teamwork is able to achieve more than the individual. The same sense of teamwork was achieved by playing in the school and local youth orchestras. However, it needed an "act of God" to turn an enthusiastic, but academically unremarkable schoolboy into a Fellow of the Royal College of Surgeons of England!

Two compulsory years in the Army on leaving school disciplined me and gave me time to realise that to achieve anything in life, particularly in a professional way, was going to mean much hard work and determined application. So I had better get down to it! I studied hard all week and several hours each evening and played rugby and cricket throughout my time at medical school at weekends. I trusted that God would see me through. Perhaps to my surprise, I passed my exams, including both parts of the Fellowship of Surgeons at the first attempt. The first part of my boyhood dream had come true. At the age of thirty I was a surgeon in the making. And now God fulfilled the second part of my dream which was that I might meet and marry the "right girl for me." A wife to love and cherish who would give our children the same standards as we had been given ourselves. We have known each other for over thirty years and we will celebrate our silver wedding in two years time. She has continued to support me day by day through many difficulties and joyful times. She has been at the centre of a stable, happy home that has been so important in enabling me to do my work with its demands on my time.

The third part of my boyhood dream was to play international rugby as my uncle and cousin had done. This ambition was achieved when I was selected to play for English Schoolboys against our French counterparts in April 1949 at Gloucester.

Returning, now, to my mailbag. This next letter, which is one of my favourites, goes further in explaining my motivation in life. It is from the younger brother of a nine year old boy who had a major operation two years previously.

"I would like to thank you for what you did to Spencer. For taking care of Spencer and for keeping him alive. For saving his life and for making him well. But he cannot go on apperators at school. Lots and lots of love, Andrew."

What a wonderful expression of love for his older brother, and what a humbling reprimand for his surgeon ("but he cannot go on apparatus at school!") Perhaps in his younger brother's view we have not achieved as much as we might. So I wrote and explained this to Andrew, that in time, after full recovery, Spencer should be fully active again.
What are we hoping for as a result of heart surgery?

Certainly, survival, but much more; a full life, a complete life, abundant life. This is expressed in my next letter from the parents of the bionic man mark II.

"We would like to try to thank you for giving us the most precious Christmas gift we could ask for. That is to see Paul full of life and bursting with energy. He has given himself the title Paul Bionic mark II. We will never be able to thank you enough, but we know you are pleased as we could see in your face when he was dashing up the ward."

What was it I wonder, they saw in my face?

Perhaps I looked pleased because of the "singing bird" that dwells within us when we are in unison with our calling in life when we are accomplishing, our own special mission that each one of us must search for in our own life and in our own particular way.

One mother wrote to me about this "singing bird."

"It is with deep appreciation and my grateful thanks I send to you for helping Andrew towards a better life. Also a big thank you to all the doctors, sisters, nurses in ward six and theatre nursing staff day and night. The anaesthetists, technicians and all the wonderful people who work behind the scenes so to speak that as a parent we don't always see. It is difficult to express what we really feel but I wouldn't like to leave any one person out. The other day I read a Chinese proverb that seems appropriate:

Keep a green branch in your heart and a singing bird will come.

Thanking the whole heart care unit team once again, for bringing the "singing bird."

Enclosed my donation, which I know isn't a great lot,
Yours sincerely."

What is this better life that Mrs Martin recognises in Andrew?
It is a full life, a balanced life, life in abundance. It is the development of the whole being as a complete unit which includes the body, our minds and our spirits or souls.

What about the soul?

Your soul is not your heart. It is your consciousness, your conscience, your feelings, your response to your fellows. It is the spirit in you which draws you to greatness, your enthusiasm, your love of life. It is that part of you which is spirit and is of God. In the second chapter of Genesis verse seven, we read

"And the Lord God formed Man of the dust of the ground and breathed into his nostrils the breath of life and he became a living soul." The soul is nourished and develops as Man allows God's grace to work in his being and in his activities. We should learn to nourish our souls through music, art, nature, sport, work, service, unselfishness, creativity, love and through worship.

As we journey through life, joy and sorrow come to us. Often we have to lose something before we appreciate its value. This is true of our health, for instance. Joy and sorrow are the very stuff of life and the greater our experience of them, the richer will be our character and the more valuable will be our citizenship. One interpretation of life which helps me in my work day by day is stated in the prayer of St Theresa,

"Christ has no body now on earth but yours. No hands but yours, no feet but yours, yours are the eyes through which to look out, Christ's compassion to the world, yours are the feet with which He is to go about doing good, and yours are the hands with which He is to bless us now."

Our final dip into the post bag pulls out a letter from the Headmaster of a very small school in a lovely village on the borders of Shropshire and Staffordshire. He writes,

"It is normal for us to give the Christmas collection to a worthwhile fund. The reason for the RLCH being chosen, is that one of our children was operated on successfully. In fact this child is so well now and so chatty we would have parcelled him up and sent him along with the money and Green Shield stamps, but the Post Office in this area are worried about brown paper parcels that wriggle."

A brown paper parcel that wriggles is alive! How alive are you and how alive am I? Have we got the balance of life right? The balance between body (physical), mind (intellect) and spirit (soul) should be like an equilateral triangle.

Jesus gave His disciples another interpretation of life.

"If any man will come after me (follow me) let him deny himself and take up his cross and follow me. For whosoever will save his life will lose it, and whosoever will lose his life for my sake shall save it. For what is a man profited, if he should gain the whole world and lose his own soul? Or what shall a man give in exchange for his soul?"

I wonder what schoolboy dreams are yours for the future? What is to be your mission in life? Mine was a mission that seemed to me to be impossible, to become a surgeon. But then I was forgetting "Thunderbolts and Acts of God!"

A CHILD'S GUIDE TO A WONKY HEART

The Lord Mayor of Liverpool entertained the whole heart team from the Royal Liverpool Children's Hospital at a party that was held in the Town Hall. I presented this poem to the assembled company as a summary of a child's experiences at the time of heart surgery.

"If your life has just begun or several years have come and gone,
Are you puffed with ankles fat or are you blue and prone to squat?
If pulse is small or not at all, don't give up hope nor grieve nor greet
consult the team at Myrtle Street.

Your diagnosis is so slick and Auntie Jean and Uncle Dick
with stethoscope and ECG and phonocardiography
your shunt will deftly demonstrate,
they'll tell you when your P wave's late
and if your output's rather low, give Isuprel to speed the flow.

You may come under Uncle Jim with catheter that's long and thin
Your inmost secrets he'll reveal, nothing from him you'll conceal
Your heart's to him an open book, he'll enter every secret nook
He may be here for Uncle Bob, but in his hands, your heart will throb.

When its very hard to say, and ASD, or PDA,
is there mitral valve stenosis
Or just a mother's deep neurosis? A hole is nothing very much
An absent septum, well, that's tough. When we find it hard to know
And furrows pucker every brow,
Uncle Ray provides the key with cine cardiography

You need an operation, son, to give you strength to ski and run.
We'll send you home but have you back,
to sleep, induced by Uncle Jack
His needle is so short and thin, you will hardly feel it going in.
There's no escape, your tongue is tied for every muscle is paralysed.

Your fears and doubts I can allay,
you're safe and sound with Auntie Kay.
Her team wear sterile gloves and masks

148

and never fail to count the swabs.
The drama's only just begun, now Philip's pump is on the run.
Your chest is open very wide so visitors can see inside!

The surgeons soon get down to work, their scalpel flashes like a dirk.
With scissors, sutures, bits of string, your heart they're reconditioning.
You look quite dead and parted from us,
and would be but for Uncle Thomas.
With bubble bag and bits of pipe he now supplies your breath of life.

Surprise, surprise, what do you think?
You came here blue but now you're pink.
So close your eyes and rest your head,
your post-op guardian's Uncle Stead.
Your nursing angels do have names, Leddy, Joe and Barbara James.
New life for you can now begin for Swindlehurst and Auntie Winn
Hatton, Poval, Blake and Allan make up the team by rule of Salmon.

So off you go, run out and play, you owe a lot to JD Hay.
For though he's now Emeritus, it all began with little fuss.
When he was surgeon FRE struck up the band to set you free.

People who will look after you when you are in hospital:

Auntie Jean	Dr Jean Shackleton	Clinical Paediatrician
Uncle Dick	Dr RS Jones	Clinical Physiology
Uncle Jim	Dr JLC Wilkinson	Cardiologist
Uncle Bob	Dr Robert Arnold	Cardiologist
Uncle Ray	Dr R Galloway	Radiologist
Uncle Jack	Dr G Jackson Rees	Anaesthetist
Auntie Kay	Sister Dickinson	Operating Theatre
Phil	Philip Waterhouse	Perfusionist
Uncle Tom	Dr Thomas Abbott	Anaesthetist
Leddy, Joe, Barbara James		Post Op nurses
Swindlehurst, Auntie Winn, Hatton, Poval, Blake and Allan		I C U Nurses
Salmon Nursing Administration		

Royal Liverpool Children's Hospital, Myrtle Street